Biology

Teaching Resources
Unit 6

PEARSON

Prentice
Hall

Upper Saddle River, New Jersey
Boston, Massachusetts

Pearson Prentice Hall™ is a trademark of Pearson Education, Inc.
Pearson® is a registered trademark of Pearson plc.
Prentice Hall® is a registered trademark of Pearson Education, Inc.

ISBN 0-13-203401-8

2 3 4 5 6 7 8 9 10   10 09 08 07

To the Teacher

The Teaching Resources unit booklets have been designed to help you teach *Prentice Hall Biology*. Each unit book consists of materials that have been designed to stimulate students' interest in biology, develop their critical thinking, and teach them basic science skills. The unit books will accommodate a wide range of student abilities and interests.

Each teaching resource unit book contains the following:

- Lesson Plans (for each section)
- Reading and Study Workbook A (includes section summaries, section worksheets, and a chapter vocabulary review written at grade level)
- Adapted Reading and Study Workbook B worksheets (Includes section summaries, key concept worksheets, and a chapter vocabulary review written at a sixth-grade reading level)
- Section Review Worksheets
- Enrichment Worksheets
- Graphic Organizers
- Chapter Tests (Includes two tests for each chapter—Test A for students performing on or above grade level; Test B for students performing on or below grade level)
- Unit Tests (two tests for each unit—Test A and Test B)
- Answer Key (for section review worksheets, enrichment worksheets, graphic organizers, and chapter tests.)
- Graphic Organizer Transparencies (generic reproducible masters)
- Transparency Planner (Full-color preview of all the transparencies that support the unit)

Unit 6 Microorganisms and Fungi
Chapter 19 Bacteria and Viruses

Chapter 20 Protists

Chapter 21 Fungi

LESSON PLAN 19–1 (pages 471–477)

Bacteria

Time
2 periods
1 block

Section Objectives

Local Standards

- **19.1.1 Explain** how the two groups of prokaryotes differ.
- **19.1.2 Describe** the factors that are used to identify prokaryotes.
- **19.1.3 Explain** why bacteria are vital to maintaining the living world.

Vocabulary prokaryote • bacillus • coccus • spirillum • chemoheterotroph • photoheterotroph • photoautotroph • chemoautotroph • obligate aerobe • obligate anaerobe • facultative anaerobe • binary fission • conjugation • endospore • nitrogen fixation

---

1 FOCUS

Reading Strategy
Students make an outline of the section, using the blue headings for the main level.

Targeted Resources
❏ Transparencies: **282** Section 19–1 Interest Grabber, **283** Section 19–1 Outline, **284** Concept Map

---

2 INSTRUCT

Use Visuals: Figure 19–2
Use Figure 19–2 to reinforce the difference between prokaryotic and eukaryotic cells. **L1** **L2**

Build Science Skills: Observing
Students use microscopes to observe prepared slides of a variety of bacteria. **L2** **L3**

Build Science Skills: Forming Operational Definitions
Review the definition of word parts used in terms that describe prokaryotes, and have students write definitions. **L1** **L2**

Demonstration
Demonstrate that bacteria can survive harsh conditions. Freeze soil overnight and then culture soil bacteria in a petri dish. **L1** **L2**

Build Science Skills: Observing
Stain a sample of yogurt mixture, and have students observe *Lactobacillus* bacteria under a microscope. **L1** **L2**

Targeted Resources
❏ Reading and Study Workbook: Section 19–1
❏ Adapted Reading and Study Workbook: Section 19–1
❏ Teaching Resources: Section Summaries, Worksheets 19–1
❏ Transparencies: **285** The Structure of a Eubacterium
❏ Lab Worksheets: Chapter 19 Exploration
❏ Lab Manual B: Chapter 19 Lab
❏ **NSTA** *sci*$_{LINKS}$ Bacteria

---

3 ASSESS

Evaluate Understanding
Have students explain the difference between eubacteria and archaebacteria.

Reteach
Use Figure 19–2 to review the basic structure and function of prokaryotes.

Targeted Resources
❏ Teaching Resources: Section Review 19–1
❏ *i***Text** Section 19–1

LESSON PLAN 19–2 (pages 478–483)

Viruses

Time
1 period
1/2 block

Section Objectives

- **19.2.1 Describe** the structure of a virus.
- **19.2.2 Explain** how viruses cause infection.

Vocabulary virus • capsid • bacteriophage • lytic infection • lysogenic infection • prophage • retrovirus

Local Standards

1 FOCUS

Vocabulary Preview
Students skim the section for the boldface terms and record the definitions.

Targeted Resources
- ❑ Transparencies: **286** Section 19–2 Interest Grabber
- ❑ Transparencies: **287** Section 19–2 Outline

2 INSTRUCT

Use Visuals: Figure 19–9
Use Figure 19–9 to review the structure of viruses. **L2**

Build Science Skills: Using Analogies
Have students expand on the analogy of how a lytic infection is like an outlaw taking over a town. **L1 L2**

Use Visuals: Figure 19–10
Use Figure 19–10 to reinforce an understanding of lytic and lysogenic infections. **L2**

Quick Lab
Students make models to investigate how viruses differ in structure. **L1 L2**

Use Visuals: Figure 19–11
Use Figure 19–11 to review differences between viruses and living cells. **L1 L2**

Targeted Resources
- ❑ Reading and Study Workbook: Section 19–2
- ❑ Adapted Reading and Study Workbook: Section 19–2
- ❑ Teaching Resources: Section Summaries, Worksheets 19–2
- ❑ Transparencies: **288** Figure 19–9 Virus Structures, **289** Figure 19–10 Lytic and Lysogenic Infections, **290** Figure 19–11 Viruses and Cells
- ❑ Biodetectives DVD: "Influenza: Tracking a Virus"
- ❑ **NSTA** sci_{LINKS} Lytic Cycle

3 ASSESS

Evaluate Understanding
Students make two flowcharts to show two examples of the way viruses infect cells.

Reteach
Have students compare the virus structures in Figure 19–9 with the bacterium structure in Figure 19–2.

Targeted Resources
Teaching Resources: Section Review 19–2
- ❑ **i Text** Section 19–2

LESSON PLAN 19–3 (pages 485–490)

Time
1 period
1/2 block

Diseases Caused by Bacteria and Viruses

Section Objectives

Local Standards

- **19.3.1 Explain** how bacteria cause disease.
- **19.3.2 Describe** how bacterial growth can be controlled.
- **19.3.3 Explain** how viruses cause disease.

Vocabulary pathogen • vaccine • antibiotic • viroid • prion

1 FOCUS

Reading Strategy
Students rewrite the blue headings as questions about bacteria and viruses.

Targeted Resources
- ❑ Transparencies: **291** Section 19–3 Interest Grabber
- ❑ Transparencies: **292** Section 19–3 Outline

2 INSTRUCT

Use Visuals: Figure 19–12
Have students review Louis Pasteur's experiment, as described in Section 1–2. **L1** **L2**

Build Science Skills: Observing
Students investigate bacteria on the body by using swabs and creating cell cultures. **L2** **L3**

Build Science Skills: Designing Experiments
Students design an experiment to test the hypothesis that hand washing reduces bacteria on the hand. **L2** **L3**

Use Visuals: Figure 19–15
Use Figure 19–15 to review differences in how diseases are spread. **L1** **L2**

Build Science Skills: Comparing and Contrasting
Students organize information in a table about viruses, viroids, and prions. **L1** **L2**

Targeted Resources
- ❑ Reading and Study Workbook: Section 19–3
- ❑ Adapted Reading and Study Workbook: Section 19–3
- ❑ Transparencies: **293** Common Diseases Caused by Bacteria, **294** Common Diseases Caused by Viruses
- ❑ Teaching Resources: Section Summaries, Worksheets Section 19–3, Enrichment
- ❑ Investigations in Forensics: Investigation 6
- ❑ Laboratory Manual A: Chapter 19 Lab
- ❑ **PHSchool.com** Career links

3 ASSESS

Evaluate Understanding
Ask students to explain why antibiotics are used to treat bacterial but not viral diseases.

Reteach
Students make a public-health pamphlet that focuses on prevention and treatment of bacterial and viral diseases.

Targeted Resources
- ❑ Teaching Resources: Section Review 19–3, Chapter Vocabulary Review, Graphic Organizer, Chapter 19 Tests: Levels A and B
- ❑ **iText** Section 19–3, Chapter 19 Assessment
- ❑ **PHSchool.com** Online Chapter 19 Test

Chapter 19 Bacteria and Viruses

Summary

19–1 Bacteria

The smallest and most common microorganisms are prokaryotes. **Prokaryotes** are unicellular and lack a nucleus. There are two kingdoms of prokaryotes: eubacteria and archaebacteria.

- Eubacteria live almost everywhere. Most eubacteria have a cell wall that contains the carbohydrate peptidoglycan. Inside the cell wall is a cell membrane that surrounds the cytoplasm.
- Archaebacteria look like eubacteria, but they have some differences. **Archaebacteria do not have peptidoglycan in their cell walls. They have many different membrane lipids. Also, the DNA sequences of key archaebacterial genes are more like those of eukaryotes than those of eubacteria.** Archaebacteria may be the ancestors of eukaryotes.

Prokaryotes are identified by characteristics that include the following:

- **Shape** Prokaryotes have three different shapes: rod-shaped (bacilli), sphere-shaped (cocci), or spiral-shaped (spirilla).
- **Chemical makeup of cell walls** Prokaryotes have two types of cell walls. Gram staining is used to tell them apart. Gram-positive bacteria appear violet when stained. Gram-negative bacteria appear pink.
- **Means of movement** Prokaryotes move in a variety of ways.
- **Means of getting energy** Most prokaryotes are heterotrophs, organisms that get energy by consuming food. Other prokaryotes are autotrophs, organisms that make their own food.

Prokaryotes get energy through cellular respiration and fermentation.

- **Obligate aerobes** need a constant oxygen supply in order to live.
- **Obligate anaerobes** do not need oxygen, and may be killed by it.
- **Facultative anaerobes** can survive with or without oxygen.

Bacteria reproduce asexually by **binary fission.** When a bacterium has grown to nearly double its size, it replicates its DNA and divides in half. Bacteria also reproduce by **conjugation.** During conjugation, genetic material is transferred from one bacterium to another. Many bacteria can form an **endospore** when conditions are bad. An endospore is a thick internal wall that surrounds the DNA and part of the cytoplasm of the bacterium. The spore can survive harsh conditions that would kill the bacterium in its active form.

Bacteria are vital to the living world. Some are producers that carry out photosynthesis. Others are decomposers that break down dead matter. Some soil bacteria convert nitrogen gas into a form that plants can use through a process called nitrogen fixation. Humans use bacteria in industry, food production, and other ways.

19–2 Viruses

Viruses are particles of nucleic acid and protein. Some contain lipids, too. A typical virus is made of a core of DNA or RNA surrounded by a protein coat called a capsid.

To reproduce, a virus must invade, or infect, a living host cell. Viruses that infect bacteria are called bacteriophages. After a virus enters a host cell, one of two processes may occur.

- In a lytic infection, a virus attaches itself to a host cell. It injects its DNA into the cell. The host cell starts making messenger RNA from the viral DNA. The messenger RNA takes over the host cell. Copies of viral DNA and the viral protein coats are made and assembled into new viruses. Then, the host cell bursts and the new viruses infect other cells.
- In a lysogenic infection, the virus does not reproduce immediately after infecting the host cell. Instead, the nucleic acid of the virus is inserted into the DNA of the host cell. The viral DNA may stay within the host DNA for quite some time. However, eventually it may become active, remove itself from the host DNA, and begin the production of new viruses.

Some viruses, called retroviruses, contain RNA as their genetic information. They produce a DNA copy of their RNA genes when they infect a cell. AIDS is a disease caused by a retrovirus.

Viruses are parasites. They must infect a living cell in order to reproduce. Because viruses are not made up of cells and cannot live on their own, viruses are not considered to be living.

19–3 Diseases Caused by Bacteria and Viruses

Some bacteria and viruses can be pathogens. Pathogens are disease-causing agents.

Bacterial Disease
Bacteria can cause tuberculosis, strep throat, and tetanus. Bacteria cause disease in two general ways.

1. Bacteria break down cells for food.

2. Bacteria release toxins (poisons) that disrupt normal body functions in the host.

To prevent some bacterial diseases, vaccines are used. A **vaccine** is a preparation of weakened or killed pathogens. A vaccine works by prompting the body to form immunity to a disease. **Immunity** is the body's natural way of killing pathogens.

When a bacterial infection occurs, antibiotics may help fight the disease. **Antibiotics** are compounds that block the growth and reproduction of bacteria.

Bacterial growth can be controlled. **Sterilization, disinfectants, and proper food storage and food processing can control bacteria.** Disinfectants include soaps and cleaning solutions. Food storage includes using a refrigerator.

Not all bacteria are pathogens. Some live in and on the human body and help it carry out needed functions. For example, bacteria that live in the intestines make vitamin K.

Viral Disease

Like bacteria, viruses cause disease by disrupting the body's normal equilibrium, or balance. In many viral infections, viruses attack and destroy certain body cells. This causes the symptoms of the disease. Viral diseases in humans include the common cold, influenza, AIDS, chickenpox, and measles. Some viral diseases can be prevented with vaccines. Viruses also cause diseases in animals and plants.

Two viruslike particles also can cause disease.

- **Viroids** are single-stranded RNA molecules that have no surrounding capsids. Viroids cause disease in plants.
- **Prions** are particles containing only protein—there is no DNA or RNA. Prions cause disease in animals, including humans.

Prokaryote Structure

A prokaryote is a unicellular organism that lacks a nucleus. Most prokaryotes have a cell wall, a cell membrane, and cytoplasm. The bacterium below is one example of a prokaryote.

Follow the prompts to locate structures in a typical bacterium.
- Color the cell membrane yellow.
- Color the cell wall blue.
- Color the flagella red.
- Color the pili orange.
- Color the DNA green.

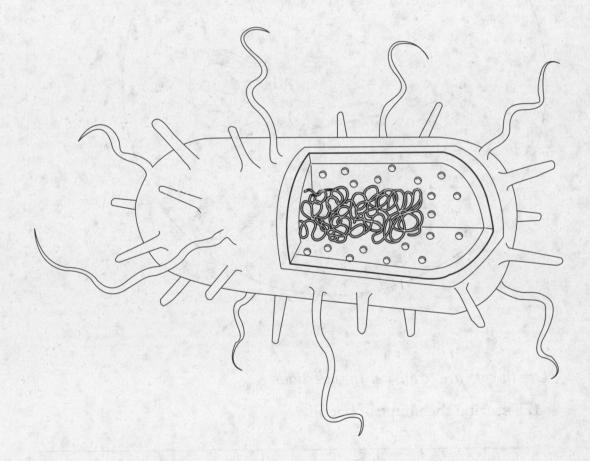

Use the diagram to answer the questions. Circle the correct answer.

1. What does the bacterium use to move?

   pili   flagellum

2. What is the bacterium's genetic material called?

   cell membrane   DNA

Bacteria Shapes

The picture shows several kinds of bacteria. Color the bacilli *blue. Color the* cocci *red. Color the* spirilla *yellow.*

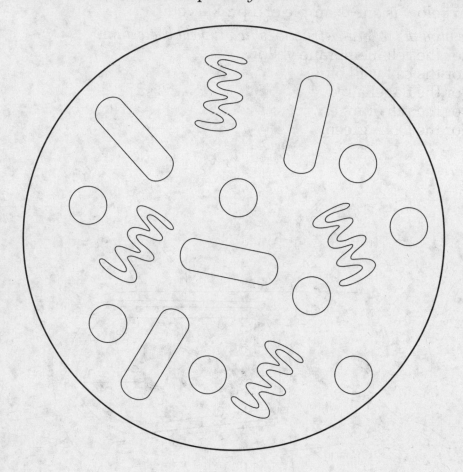

Use the picture to answer the questions.

1. Describe the shape of bacilli.

_____

2. Describe the shape of cocci.

_____

3. Describe the shape of spirilla.

_____

What Makes Up a Virus?

Viruses are particles made up of protein, genetic material, and sometimes lipids. The genetic material in a virus can be RNA or DNA. The protein coat that surrounds the genetic material is called the capsid.

The diagrams show three kinds of viruses. Circle the genetic material in each virus. Color the protein parts of each virus yellow.

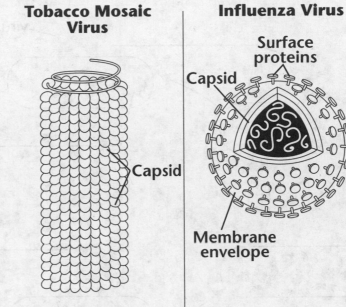

T4 Bacteriophage

Head

Tail sheath

Tail fiber

Tobacco Mosaic Virus

Capsid

Influenza Virus

Surface proteins

Capsid

Membrane envelope

Use the diagrams to answer the questions.

1. Where is the genetic material in a T4 bacteriophage located?

_____

_____

2. In general, is the genetic material in a virus inside or outside the protein parts?

_____

3. Which structure contains proteins that enable a virus to enter a host cell? Circle the correct answer.

capsid   RNA

Lytic Infections

A bacteriophage is a virus that can infect bacteria. A lytic infection is one kind of viral infection. It results in lysis, or bursting of the host cell. The diagram shows how a bacteriophage causes a lytic infection in a bacterium.

Label the bacterial DNA, host bacterium, viral DNA, and virus. Then, circle the step that shows lysis of the host cell.

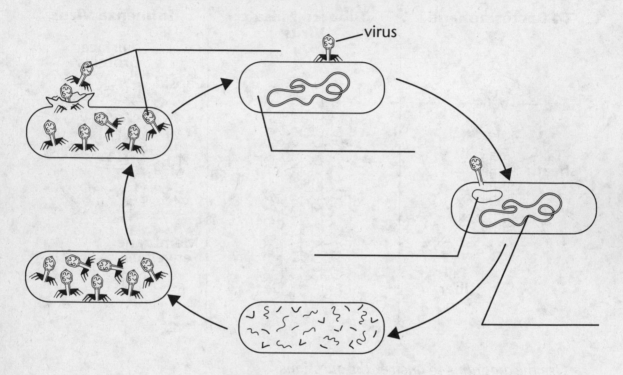

Use the diagram to answer the questions.

1. Summarize what happens in a lytic infection.

   _____

   _____

   _____

2. What is one result of a lytic infection? Circle the correct answer.

   lysis of the virus   lysis of the host cell

Lysogenic Infections

A lysogenic infection occurs when viral DNA inserts itself into the DNA of the host cell. The viral DNA is replicated along with the host cell DNA. Eventually, the viral DNA will separate out of the host DNA and direct the construction of new virus particles. The diagram shows how a bacteriophage causes a lysogenic infection in a bacterium.

Circle the viral DNA in each diagram of the bacterium.

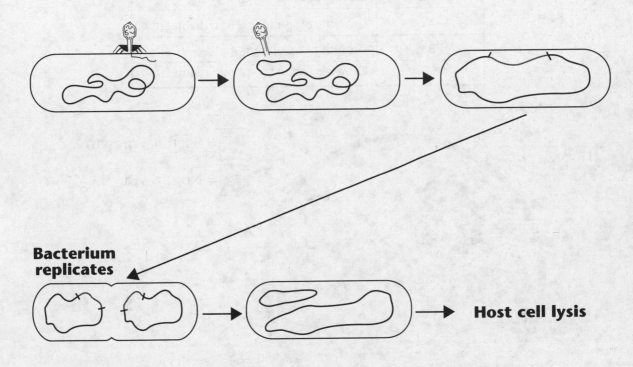

Use the diagram to answer the questions.

1. What happens after the viral DNA is inserted into the bacterial DNA?

   _____

   _____

2. How does a lysogenic infection help a virus spread?

   _____

   _____

Antibiotics

Antibiotics are compounds that block the growth and reproduction of bacteria. The picture shows a petri dish of bacteria with three antibiotic disks in it.

Use the picture and the table to label each disk with the letter of the antibiotic used on it.

Effects of Antibiotics	
Antibiotic	Observation After One Week
A	Growth stopped for 6 mm diameter
B	Growth not stopped
C	Growth stopped for 2 mm diameter

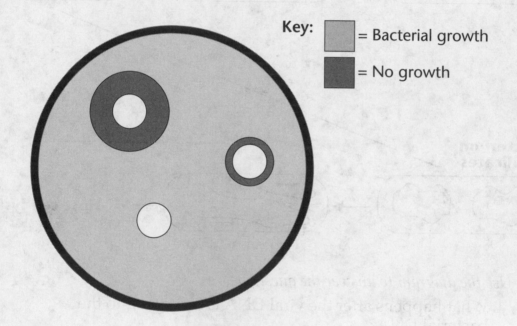

Key:
 = Bacterial growth
 = No growth

Use the picture and table to answer the questions.

1. Which antibiotic was most effective against the bacteria in the petri dish?

_____

2. Why did you choose that antibiotic?

_____

Chapter 19 Bacteria and Viruses

Vocabulary Review

Matching *In the space provided, write the letter of the definition that best matches each term.*

_____ 1. endospore

_____ 2. virus

_____ 3. coccus

_____ 4. prokaryote

_____ 5. bacillus

_____ 6. vaccine

_____ 7. spirillum

a. bacterium with a rod shape
b. bacterium with a corkscrew shape
c. particle of nucleic acid, protein, and possibly lipids that can reproduce only by infecting other cells
d. unicellular organism that lacks a nucleus
e. preparation of weakened or killed pathogen that, when injected, may prompt the body to develop an immunity to the disease
f. bacterium with a sphere shape
g. thick internal wall produced by a bacterium when growth conditions become unfavorable

Matching *In the space provided, write the letter of the definition that best matches each term.*

_____ 8. bacteriophage

_____ 9. retrovirus

_____ 10. prion

_____ 11. capsid

_____ 12. lytic

_____ 13. binary fission

_____ 14. conjugation

a. exchange of genetic material in bacteria
b. infectious protein particle
c. type of viral infection that causes the cell to burst
d. protein coat of a virus
e. virus that infects bacteria
f. asexual form of reproduction carried out by bacteria
g. virus having RNA as its genetic material

Summary

19–1 Bacteria

The smallest and most common microorganisms are prokaryotes, which are unicellular organisms that lack a nucleus. Prokaryotes are divided into two kingdoms: Eubacteria and Archaebacteria. Eubacteria live almost everywhere. Eubacteria are usually surrounded by a cell wall, which contains a carbohydrate called peptidoglycan. Inside the cell wall is a cell membrane that surrounds the cytoplasm. Archaebacteria look very similar to eubacteria. Archaebacteria lack the peptidoglycan of eubacteria and have different membrane lipids. Also, the DNA sequences of key archaebacterial genes are more like those of eukaryotes than those of eubacteria. Archaebacteria may be the ancestors of eukaryotes.

Prokaryotes are identified by characteristics such as shape, the chemical nature of their cell walls, the way they move, and the way they obtain energy. Three differently shaped prokaryotes are bacilli, cocci, and spirilla. Bacilli (singular: bacillus) are rod-shaped; cocci (singular: coccus) are sphere-shaped; and spirilla (singular: spirillum) are spiral or corkscrew-shaped. Two different types of cell walls are found in prokaryotes. A method called Gram staining is used to tell them apart. Gram-positive bacteria appear violet when stained, while Gram-negative bacteria appear pink. Prokaryotes move in a variety of ways.

Most prokaryotes are heterotrophs—organisms that obtain energy by consuming other organisms. Other prokaryotes are autotrophs, organisms that can make their own food. Heterotrophic prokaryotes include chemoheterotrophs and photoheterotrophs. Autotrophic prokaryotes include photoautotrophs and chemoautotrophs.

Prokaryotes release energy by both cellular respiration and fermentation. Organisms that require a constant supply of oxygen to live are called obligate aerobes. Organisms that do not require oxygen are called obligate anaerobes. Organisms that can survive with or without oxygen are called facultative anaerobes.

When a bacterium has grown so that it has nearly doubled, it replicates its DNA and divides in half, producing two identical "daughter" cells. This asexual reproduction is called binary fission. Bacteria are also able to exchange genetic information by a process called conjugation. Many bacteria can form an endospore when conditions are bad.

Bacteria are vital to maintaining the living world. Some are producers that carry out photosynthesis. Others are decomposers that break down dead matter. Some soil bacteria convert natural nitrogen gas into a form plants can use through a process called nitrogen fixation. Humans use bacteria in industry, food production, and other ways.

19–2 Viruses

Viruses are particles of nucleic acid, protein, and, in some cases, lipids. All viruses have one thing in common: They enter living cells and, once inside, use the machinery of the infected cell to produce more viruses. A typical virus is composed of a core of DNA or RNA surrounded by a protein coat. A virus's protein coat is called its capsid. Viruses that infect bacteria are called bacteriophages.

Once the virus is inside a host cell, two different infection processes may occur. In a lytic infection, a virus enters a cell, makes copies of itself, and causes the cell to burst, releasing new virus particles that can attack other cells. The virus uses the materials of the host cell to make copies of its own DNA molecule. In a lysogenic infection, a virus integrates its DNA into the DNA of the host cell, and the viral genetic information replicates along with the host cell's DNA. The viral DNA that is embedded in the host's DNA is called a prophage. The prophage may remain part of the DNA of the host cell for many generations. Eventually, the prophage will remove itself from the host cell DNA and make new virus particles.

Some viruses, called retroviruses, contain RNA as their genetic information. In a retrovirus, the genetic information is copied backward—from RNA to DNA instead of from DNA to RNA. The virus that causes the disease AIDS is a retrovirus.

Viruses must infect a living cell in order to reproduce. Viruses are parasites. Because viruses are not made up of cells and cannot live independently, viruses are not considered to be living things.

19–3 Diseases Caused by Bacteria and Viruses

Disease-causing agents are known as pathogens. Bacteria and viruses can cause disease. Not all bacteria are pathogens. Some live in and on the human body and help the body perform essential functions. Other bacteria can produce human diseases such as tuberculosis, strep throat, and tooth decay.

Bacteria produce disease in one of two general ways. Some bacteria damage the cells and tissues of the infected organism directly by breaking down the cells for food. Other bacteria release toxins (poisons) that travel throughout the body interfering with the normal activity of the host.

Many bacterial diseases can be prevented by using a vaccine. A vaccine is a preparation of weakened or killed pathogens. A vaccine can prompt the body to produce immunity to the disease. Immunity is the body's natural way of killing pathogens. When a bacterial infection does occur, antibiotics can be used to fight the disease. Antibiotics are compounds that block the growth and reproduction of bacteria. Animals also suffer from bacterial diseases.

There are various methods to control bacterial growth, including sterilization, disinfectants, and food storage and food processing. Disinfectants include soaps and cleaning solutions. Food storage includes using a refrigerator.

Viruses produce disease by disrupting the body's normal equilibrium. In many viral infections, viruses attack and destroy certain body cells, causing the symptoms of the disease. Viral diseases in humans include the common cold, influenza, AIDS, chickenpox, and measles. Viruses produce other serious diseases in both animals and plants.

Two other viruslike particles can cause disease. Viroids are single-stranded RNA molecules that have no surrounding capsids. Viroids cause disease in plants. Prions are particles that contain only protein—there is no DNA or RNA. Prions cause disease in animals, including humans.

Section 19–1 Bacteria (pages 471–477)

⊂⊃ **Key Concepts**

- How do the two groups of prokaryotes differ?
- What factors are used to identify prokaryotes?
- What is the importance of bacteria?

Introduction (page 471)

1. What are prokaryotes? _____

_____

2. Is the following sentence true or false? Prokaryotes are much smaller than most eukaryotic cells. _____

Classifying Prokaryotes (pages 471–472)

3. What are the two different groups of prokaryotes?

a. _____   b. _____

4. Which is the larger of the two kingdoms of prokaryotes? _____

5. Where do eubacteria live? _____

_____

6. What protects a prokaryotic cell from injury? _____

_____

7. Circle the letter of what is within the cell wall of a prokaryote.

a. another cell wall   c. archaebacteria

b. cell membrane   d. pili

8. What is peptidoglycan? _____

_____

9. Some eubacteria have a second _____ outside the cell membrane.

10. Circle the letter of each sentence that is true about archaebacteria.

a. Their membrane lipids are different from those of eubacteria.

b. They lack a cell wall.

c. They lack peptidoglycan.

d. They look very similar to eubacteria.

11. What is significant about the DNA sequences of key archaebacterial genes?

_____

_____

12. How are archaebacteria related to eukaryotes? _____

13. What are methanogens, and where do they live? _____

_____

_____

Identifying Prokaryotes (page 473)

14. Use the following labels to complete the illustration of a typical prokaryote: cell membrane, cell wall, DNA, flagellum.

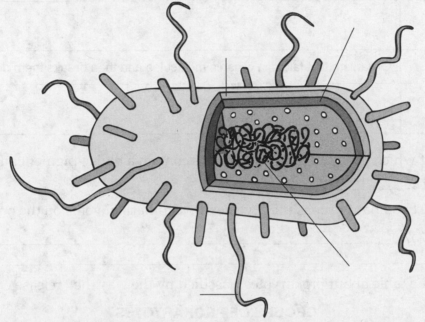

15. What are four characteristics used to identify prokaryotes?

   a. _____

   b. _____

   c. _____

   d. _____

16. What are each of the differently shaped prokaryotes called?

   a. The rod-shaped are called _____.

   b. The spherical-shaped are called _____.

   c. The corkscrew-shaped are called _____.

17. A method of telling two different types of eubacteria apart by using dyes is called

_____.

18. What colors are Gram-positive and Gram-negative bacteria under the microscope

when treated with Gram stain? _____

_____

19. What are flagella? _____

Metabolic Diversity (pages 473–474)

21. Complete the table about prokaryotes classified by the way they obtain energy.

GROUPS OF PROKARYOTES

Group	Description
	Organism that carries out photosynthesis in a manner similar to that of plants
Chemoautotroph	
	Organism that takes in organic molecules and then breaks them down
Photoheterotroph	

22. Members of which group of photoautotrophs contain a bluish pigment and chlorophyll *a*? _____

23. How do the chemoautotrophs that live near hydrothermal vents on the ocean floor obtain energy? _____

_____

24. Complete the table about prokaryotes classified by the way they release energy.

GROUPS OF PROKARYOTES

Group	Description
	Organisms that require a constant supply of oxygen
Obligate anaerobes	
Facultative anaerobes	

25. Facultative anaerobes can switch between cellular respiration and _____.

Growth and Reproduction (page 475)

26. What occurs in the process of binary fission? _____

_____

_____

27. What occurs during conjugation? _____

_____

28. Is the following sentence true or false? Most prokaryotes reproduce by conjugation.

_____

29. What is an endospore? _____
_____
_____

Importance of Bacteria (pages 476–477)

30. How do decomposers help the ecosystem recycle nutrients when a tree dies?
_____
_____
_____

31. What would happen to plants and animals if decomposers did not recycle nutrients?
_____
_____

32. Why do plants and animals need nitrogen? _____
_____
_____

33. How does nitrogen fixation help plants? _____

34. What kind of relationship do many plants have with nitrogen-fixing bacteria?
_____

35. How can bacteria be used to clean up an oil spill? _____
_____

36. What have biotechnology companies begun to realize about bacteria adapted
to extreme environments? _____
_____
_____

Reading Skill Practice

Writing a summary can help you remember the information you have read. When
you write a summary, write only the most important points. Write a summary of the
information under the green heading Decomposers. Your summary should be
shorter than the text on which it is based. Do your work on a separate sheet of paper.

Section 19–2 Viruses (pages 478–483)

🔑 Key Concepts
- What is the structure of a virus?
- How do viruses cause infection?

What Is a Virus? (pages 478–479)

1. What are viruses? _____

_____

2. What do all viruses have in common? _____

_____

_____

3. Is the following sentence true or false? Most viruses are so small that they can be seen only with the aid of a powerful electron microscope. _____

4. What is the structure of a typical virus? _____

_____

5. Complete the illustration of a T4 bacteriophage by labeling the parts.

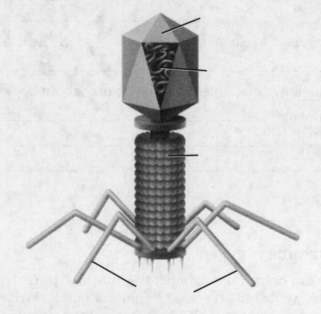

6. A virus's protein coat is called a(an) _____.

7. How does a typical virus get inside a cell? _____

_____

_____

8. What occurs when viruses get inside cells? _____

_____

_____

_____

9. Why are most viruses highly specific to the cells they infect? _____

_____

_____

10. What are bacteriophages? _____

Viral Infection (pages 480–481)

11. Why is a lytic infection given that name? _____

_____

12. Circle the letter of each sentence that is true about a lysogenic infection.

    a. The virus lyses the host cell immediately.

    b. The virus embeds its DNA into the host's DNA.

    c. The virus's DNA is replicated along with the host cell's DNA.

    d. A host cell makes copies of the virus indefinitely.

13. Complete the flowchart about a lytic infection.

> The bacteriophage attaches to the bacterium's _____.

⬇

> The bacteriophage injects its _____ into the cell.

⬇

> The cell makes mRNA from the bacteriophage's _____.

⬇

> The virus wrecks the cell, causing it to _____

⬇

> The bursting of the cell releases new bacteriophage _____.

14. What is a prophage? _____

_____

Retroviruses (page 482)

15. What are retroviruses? _____

_____

16. What happens when retroviruses infect a cell? _____

_____

_____

Viruses and Living Cells (pages 482–483)

17. Circle the letter of each reason why some biologists do not consider viruses to be alive.

   a. They can't infect living cells.

   b. They can't evolve.

   c. They can't regulate gene expression.

   d. They can't reproduce independently.

18. Complete the table comparing viruses and cells.

Virus and Cells

Characteristic	Virus	Cell
Structure	DNA or RNA core, capsid	Cell membrane, cytoplasm; eukaryotes also contain nucleus and organelles
Reproduction		Independent cell division either asexually or sexually
Genetic Code		DNA
Growth and Development	No	
Obtain and Use Energy		Yes
Response to the Environment	No	
Change Over Time		

Section 19–3 Diseases Caused by Bacteria and Viruses (pages 485–490)

⊂▭⊃ **Key Concepts**

- How do bacteria cause disease?
- How can bacterial growth be controlled?
- How do viruses cause disease?

Bacterial Disease in Humans (pages 485–486)

1. What are pathogens? _____

2. What are the two general ways that bacteria cause disease?

   a. _____

   _____

   b. _____

   _____

3. What kind of tissue do the bacteria that cause tuberculosis break down?

   _____

4. What are antibiotics? _____

   _____

5. What do you think is one of the major reasons for the dramatic increase in life expectancy during the past two centuries? _____

   _____

   _____

Controlling Bacteria (pages 486–487)

6. What is sterilization? _____

7. A chemical solution that kills pathogenic bacteria is called a(an) _____.

8. Why will food stored at low temperatures keep longer? _____

   _____

   _____

Viral Disease in Humans (page 488)

9. What are some human diseases that viruses cause? _____

   _____

   _____

Viral Disease in Animals (page 489)

10. What is one example of a viral disease in animals? _____

_____

11. Cancer-causing viruses are known as _____.

Viral Disease in Plants (page 489)

12. Why do plant viruses have a difficult time entering the cells they infect? _____

_____

_____

13. How are most plant viruses spread? _____

Viroids and Prions (page 490)

14. What are viroids? _____

_____

15. A disease-causing particle that contains only protein and not DNA or RNA is called

a(an) _____.

Chapter 19   Bacteria and Viruses

Vocabulary Review

Matching   *In the space provided, write the letter of the definition that best matches each term.*

_____ 1. lysogenic infection

_____ 2. eubacteria

_____ 3. chemoautotroph

_____ 4. toxin

_____ 5. prion

_____ 6. bacteriophage

_____ 7. coccus

_____ 8. chemoheterotroph

_____ 9. antibiotic

_____ 10. virus

_____ 11. prokaryote

_____ 12. spirillum

_____ 13. prophage

_____ 14. pathogen

_____ 15. lytic infection

_____ 16. endospore

_____ 17. bacillus

_____ 18. binary fission

_____ 19. obligate anaerobe

_____ 20. vaccine

a. spiral-shaped bacterium

b. pathogen that causes disease in animals by forming a protein clump

c. rod-shaped bacterium

d. organism that must take in organic molecules for both energy and a supply of carbon

e. a particle of nucleic acid, protein, and in some cases, lipids

f. process in which viral DNA becomes part of a host cell's DNA

g. disease-causing agent

h. spherical bacterium

i. process in which a host cell bursts after being invaded by a virus

j. organism consisting of one cell that lacks a nucleus

k. process in which a bacterium replicates its DNA and divides in half

l. organism that obtains energy from inorganic molecules

m. spore formed by bacteria when growth conditions become unfavorable

n. virus that infects bacteria

o. viral DNA that is embedded in the host's DNA

p. substance produced by some bacteria that poisons host cells

q. preparation of weakened or killed pathogens

r. compound that can destroy bacteria

s. organism that can live only in an oxygen-free environment

t. the larger of the two kingdoms of prokaryotes

Chapter 19 Bacteria and Viruses   Section Review 19-1

Reviewing Key Concepts

Short Answer *On the lines provided, answer the following questions.*

1. What are three ways in which archaebacteria differ from eubacteria?

_____

_____

2. Describe four factors that are used to identify prokaryotes.

_____

_____

_____

3. What are three ways in which bacteria are vital to the living world?

_____

_____

Reviewing Key Skills

Interpreting Graphics *On the lines provided, label the diagram using the following terms:* cell wall, pili, flagellum, DNA. *Then, use the diagram to answer questions 8 and 9.*

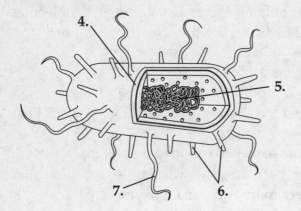

4. _____

5. _____

6. _____

7. _____

8. **Classifying** Is the bacterium in the diagram a bacillus, coccus, or spirillum? Explain your answer.

_____

9. **Predicting** How would you expect this bacterium to move?

_____

10. **Comparing and Contrasting** In prokaryotes, how are binary fission and conjugation different?

_____

_____

_____

Name_____ Class_____ Date _____

Reviewing Key Concepts

Multiple Choice *On the lines provided, write the letter of the answer that best completes each sentence.*

_____ 1. A typical virus has a core composed of
           a. capsid proteins.   c. membrane envelopes.
           b. surface proteins.   d. DNA or RNA.

_____ 2. The outer layer of a virus is composed of
           a. RNA.   c. DNA.
           b. viral genes.   d. proteins.

_____ 3. An infection in which a virus makes copies of itself
and causes the host cell to burst is called
           a. lysogenic.   c. lytic.
           b. oncogenic.   d. capsid.

_____ 4. An infection in which DNA of a virus is embedded into a
host cell and replicates with host DNA is called
           a. lysogenic.   c. lytic.
           b. oncogenic.   d. capsid.

Reviewing Key Skills

Interpreting Graphics *On the lines provided, describe what is occurring in each stage of the lytic cycle.*

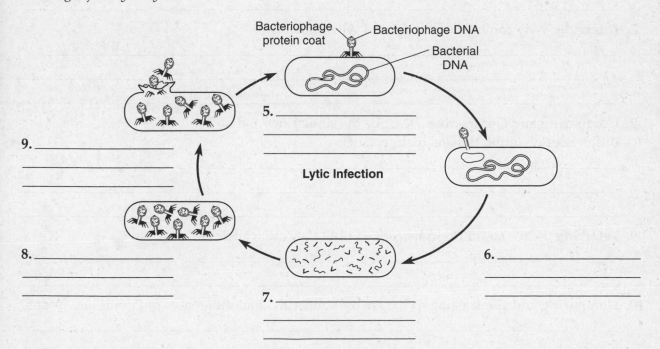

10. Applying Concepts Why are viruses not considered to be living things?

_____

_____

Reviewing Key Concepts

Completion *On the lines provided, complete the following sentences.*

1. One way that bacteria can cause disease is by breaking down and damaging _____ of the infected organism.

2. Bacteria can also cause disease by releasing _____ that harm the body.

3. A(an) _____ is a disease-causing agent.

4. One way to control bacterial growth is by subjecting them to great heat, a process called _____.

5. A(an) _____ is a preparation of weakened or killed pathogens that can prompt the body to produce immunity to a disease.

Reviewing Key Skills

6. **Comparing and Contrasting** How are the causes of tuberculosis and strep throat similar? How are they different?

   _____

   _____

   _____

   _____

7. **Inferring** Why can't viruses be treated with antibiotics?

   _____

   _____

   _____

8. **Comparing and Contrasting** Describe the similarities and differences of antibiotics and disinfectants.

   _____

   _____

   _____

9. **Inferring** Why should meats be cooked until they are well done?

   _____

   _____

10. **Comparing and Contrasting** What are the similarities and differences of viroids and prions?

   _____

   _____

   _____

   _____

   _____

Chapter 19 Bacteria and Viruses **Chapter Vocabulary Review**

Crossword Puzzle *Use the clues below and on the following page to complete the puzzle.*

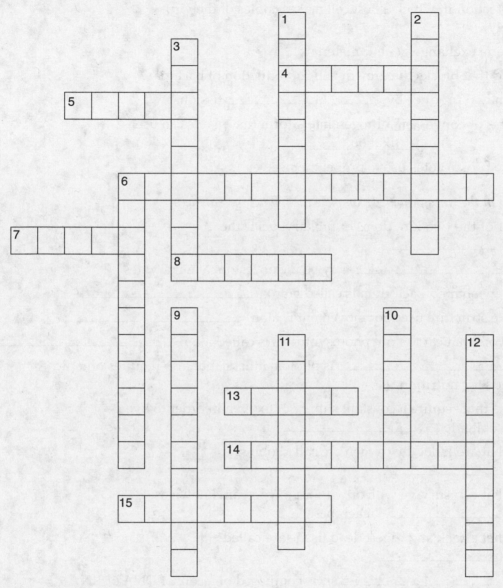

Across

4. the outer protein coat of a virus

5. particle of nucleic acid and protein that can reproduce only by infecting living cells

6. organism that obtains energy directly from inorganic molecules

7. an infectious particle made of protein rather than DNA or RNA

8. sphere-shaped bacterium

13. type of infection in which the host cell bursts and is destroyed

14. unicellular microorganism that lacks a nucleus

15. disease-causing agent

Down

1. rod-shaped bacterium
2. type of spore that can remain dormant until favorable conditions for growth arise
3. type of infection in which a host cell makes copies of the virus indefinitely
6. how bacteria exchange genetic material
9. compound that blocks the growth and reproduction of bacteria
10. Bacteria may reproduce by _____ fission.
11. The process of converting nitrogen into a form that plants can use is _____ fixation.
12. a structure prokaryotes use to propel themselves

Completion *On the lines provided, complete the following sentences.*

16. The larger of the two kingdoms of prokaryotes is the
    _____.
17. The _____ may be the ancestors of eukaryotes.
18. A corkscrew-shaped bacterium is called a(an) _____.
19. A whiplike structure used for movement is a(an) _____.
20. A prokaryote that carries out photosynthesis is called a(an) _____.
21. A(An) _____ is photosynthetic, but also requires organic compounds for nutrition.
22. Organisms that require a constant supply of oxygen in order to live are called obligate _____.
23. Bacteria that are killed by oxygen are called obligate
    _____.
24. Bacteria that can survive with or without oxygen are known as _____ anaerobes.
25. Bacteria that attack and digest dead tissue are called
    _____.
26. A typical _____ is composed of a core of DNA or RNA surrounded by a protein coat.
27. A virus that infects bacteria is called a(an) _____.
28. A virus that stores its genetic information as RNA is called a(an)
    _____.
29. A(An) _____ can be used to cure many bacterial diseases.
30. Techniques of _____ rely on extreme temperatures or chemical action to destroy bacteria.

Chapter 19 Bacteria and Viruses   Enrichment

Acid-Fast Bacteria

Almost all bacteria can be classified as Gram-positive or Gram-negative by a process called Gram staining. Very few bacteria are Gram-positive. Most bacteria, yeasts, and fungi are Gram-negative. How bacteria respond to the Gram-staining procedure can provide information about the nutritive requirements, cell wall composition, and other traits of the bacteria. When treated with special dyes, Gram-positive bacteria appear deep violet in color. Gram-negative bacteria appear pink. The Gram-staining technique can help doctors identify bacteria and choose the correct antibiotics to treat bacterial infections.

Some bacteria, however, are resistant to Gram staining. These bacteria are known as acid-fast bacteria, and are identified by using the acid-fast stain. In this procedure, a sample of unknown bacteria is dyed and then washed with acidified alcohol. This will remove most of the dye. Those bacteria that "hold fast" to the dye will be strongly stained and readily identifiable as acid-fast bacteria.

Because acid-fast bacteria are a major cause of disease, it is particularly important to be able to identify them. The acid-fast bacteria form a homogeneous group composed of the genera *Mycobacterium* and *Nocardia*. Mycobacteria are usually rod shaped, and are found in soil, water, and animals. Many species are saprophytic (feed on dead organic matter); others cause diseases such as diphtheria, tuberculosis, and leprosy.

Acid-fast bacteria are characterized by their high lipid content. Lipids and waxes make up as much as 40 percent of the dry weight of acid-fast bacteria. These lipids and waxes are the key to testing for acid-fast bacteria. The lipids and waxes absorb dye so it can't be removed with acidified alcohol. This is how acid-fast bacteria "hold fast" to dye and remain stained while bacteria are washed clean.

Evaluation *On the lines provided, answer the following questions.*

1. How are acid-fast bacteria different from other bacteria?

   _____

   _____

   _____

   _____

   _____

2. Why is it important to wash the bacteria sample after it has been dyed?

   _____

   _____

   _____

   _____

   _____

Name_____ Class_____ Date _____

Concept Map

Using information from the chapter, complete the concept map below. If there is not enough room in the concept map to write your answers, write them on a separate sheet of paper.

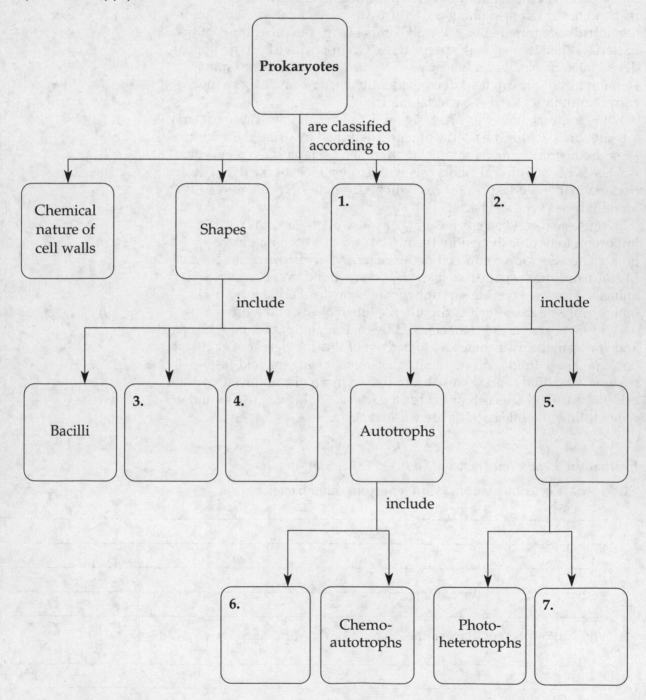

Name______________________ Class________________ Date ____________

Multiple Choice

Write the letter that best answers the question or completes the statement on the line provided.

____ **1.** Prokaryotes are unicellular organisms that lack a
a. cell wall.
b. cell membrane.
c. definite shape.
d. nucleus.

____ **2.** The structure labeled C in Figure 1 is
a. DNA.
b. an organelle.
c. the nucleus
d. a high-energy sugar.

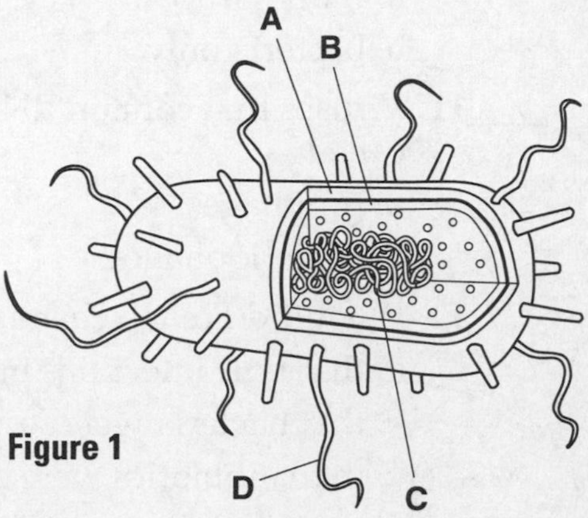

Figure 1

____ **3.** Which of the following statements is NOT true about archaebacteria?
a. They are thought to be ancestors of eukaryotes.
b. Many live in harsh environments.
c. They lack peptidoglycan in their cell wall.
d. They make up the largest kingdom of prokaryotes.

____ **4.** Spherical prokaryotes are called
a. spirilla.
b. flagella.
c. cocci.
d. bacilli.

____ **5.** When treated with Gram stain, Gram-positive bacteria appear
a. violet.
b. pink.
c. yellow.
d. orange.

____ **6.** Unlike photoautotrophs, chemoautotrophs obtain energy
a. directly from the sun.
b. directly from chemical reactions.
c. indirectly from carbon molecules.
d. indirectly from other organisms.

____ **7.** Which of the following describes a role of bacteria in the environment?
a. carrying out photosynthesis
b. recycling nutrients
c. fixing nitrogen
d. all of the above

____ **8.** Humans use bacteria in all of the following ways EXCEPT to
a. clean up small oil spills.
b. make butter and milk.
c. mine minerals from the ground.
d. synthesize drugs.

____ **9.** What is the basic structure of a virus?

    a. DNA or RNA surrounded by a protein coat

    b. a capsid surrounded by a protein coat

    c. a tail sheath surrounded by tail fibers

    d. a tiny cell surrounded by a cell wall

____ **10.** Bacteriophages infect

    a. other viruses.   c. any available host cell.

    b. bacteria only.   d. cells undergoing the lytic cycle.

____ **11.** Viruses that contain RNA as their genetic information are called

    a. prophages.   c. retroviruses.

    b. bacteriophages.   d. capsids.

____ **12.** What did French chemist Louis Pasteur help establish?

    a. that lytic infections involved cell bursting

    b. that bacteria were responsible for some diseases

    c. that antibiotics were effective against bacteria

    d. that viral diseases disrupt the body's equilibrium

____ **13.** What can a vaccine do when it is injected into the body?

    a. prompt the body to produce immunity to a disease

    b. produce toxins that disrupt bacterial equilibrium

    c. use bacterial cells for food

    d. destroy new pathogens as they arise in the body

____ **14.** Which of the following diseases is NOT caused by a virus?

    a. tetanus   c. AIDS

    b. influenza   d. chickenpox

____ **15.** Which of the following is NOT true about prions?

    a. They are particles composed only of protein.

    b. They are single-stranded RNA molecules with no capsid.

    c. They can cause disease in humans.

    d. They contain no RNA or DNA.

Completion

Complete each statement on the line provided.

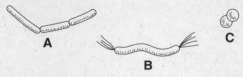

Figure 2

16. The organism labeled A in Figure 2 is an example of a(an) _____ .

17. The knoblike root nodules of soybean plants are the sites of _____ .

Name ______________________ Class ______________ Date ____________

18. In a lysogenic infection, the viral DNA that is embedded in a host cell's DNA is called a(an) ________________.

19. In Figure 3, the structure labeled A is a(an) ________________.

20. The structure labeled C in Figure 3 is ________________.

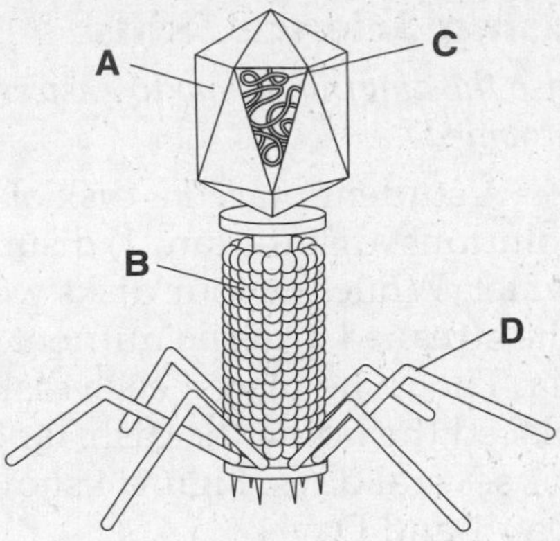

Figure 3

Short Answer

In complete sentences, write the answers to the questions on the lines provided.

21. List four factors that are used to identify prokaryotes.

____

____

____

____

22. Describe two roles that bacteria have in the environment.

____

____

____

____

23. What is a virus? Describe the basic structure of a virus.

____

____

____

____

24. Why are viruses not considered to be living things?

____

____

____

____

25. List three methods used to control bacterial growth.

____

____

____

____

Using Science Skills

Use the diagram below to answer the following questions on the lines provided.

A student placed a disk of filter paper in each of the following solutions: disinfectant 1, disinfectant 2, disinfectant 3, and distilled water. While the four disks were soaking in their respective solutions, she streaked a sterile nutrient agar dish with a culture of *E. coli* bacteria. Then, she placed each disk carefully onto the nutrient agar dish, placed the lid on the dish, taped it shut, and incubated the dish at 37°C for several days. Figure 4 shows how the nutrient agar dish looked on Day 1 and Day 4.

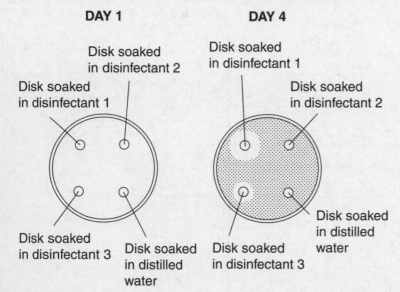

Figure 4

26. **Designing Experiments** Based on Figure 4, what is the student probably trying to test?

_____

_____

_____

_____

27. **Controlling Variables** What is the control in the experiment shown in Figure 4?

_____

_____

28. **Drawing Conclusions** How can the student measure the effectiveness of each disinfectant shown in Figure 4?

_____

_____

_____

_____

29. **Inferring** Look at the dishes in Figure 4. Which disinfectant was the most effective at controlling the growth of *E. coli?* How do you know?

_____

_____

_____

30. **Drawing Conclusions** Look at the results of the experiment shown in Figure 4. Why do you think the different disinfectants are not equally effective against the *E. coli* bacteria?

_____

_____

_____

Essay

Write the answer to each question in the space provided.

31. Explain how the two groups of prokaryotes differ.

32. What is the difference between binary fission and conjugation?

33. Briefly describe two ways that bacteriophages infect cells.

34. Describe the two ways that bacteria cause disease.

35. Contrast a bacterial disease with a viral disease.

Chapter 19 Bacteria and Viruses **Chapter Test B**

Multiple Choice

Write the letter that best answers the question or completes the statement on the line provided.

_____ 1. The microorganisms called prokaryotes are
   a. bacteria and viruses.
   b. unicellular organisms that lack a nucleus.
   c. heterotrophs that contain no DNA.

_____ 2. Which group of prokaryotes do scientists think may be ancestors of eukaryotes?
   a. monera
   b. eubacteria
   c. archaebacteria

_____ 3. Which of the following are used to identify prokaryotes?
   a. cell shape
   b. the way prokaryotes move
   c. both a and b

_____ 4. A method called Gram staining is used to tell
   a. what shape a prokaryote has.
   b. how a prokaryote obtains energy.
   c. what kind of cell wall a prokaryote has.

_____ 5. Two groups of prokaryotes that make their own food from inorganic molecules are
   a. heterotrophs and autotrophs.
   b. obligate aerobes and obligate anaerobes.
   c. photoautotrophs and chemoautotrophs.

_____ 6. Binary fission occurs when a bacterium
   a. exchanges genetic information with another cell.
   b. replicates its DNA and divides in half.
   c. forms a hollow bridge to another bacterial cell.

_____ 7. Bacteria that break down the nutrients in dead matter into simpler substances that are taken up by plant roots are called
   a. endospores.
   b. decomposers.
   c. photoautotrophs.

_____ 8. A typical virus is composed of a
   a. cell wall made of peptidoglycan.
   b. core of DNA or RNA surrounded by a protein coat.
   c. core of protein surrounded by a coat of DNA.

____ **9.** What are viruses that infect bacteria called?
   a. archaebacteria
   b. facultative anaerobes
   c. bacteriophages

_____ **10.** Viruses that contain RNA as their genetic information are
   a. bacteriophages.
   b. retroviruses.
   c. prophages.

_____ **11.** Antibiotics are compounds that can
   a. disrupt a virus's normal equilibrium.
   b. control a viral infection.
   c. block the growth and reproduction of bacteria.

_____ **12.** Which of the following is a disease caused by a virus?
   a. AIDS
   b. strep throat
   c. tooth decay

_____ **13.** If you wash your hands properly, ordinary soaps do a good job of removing
   a. bacteria.
   b. viruses.
   c. viroids.

____ **14.** Viruses have more difficulty entering plant cells than animal cells because
   a. plant cells have tough cell walls.
   b. nitrogen fixation harms plant cells.
   c. animal cells have no cell membranes.

____ **15.** A prion is a viruslike particle that contains only
   a. DNA.
   b. protein.
   c. RNA.

Completion

Complete each statement on the line provided.

16. During _____, a hollow bridge forms between two bacterial cells, and genes move from one cell to another.

17. The process of converting nitrogen into a form plants can use is called _____ .

18. A virus's protein coat is called a(an) _____ .

Name ______________________ Class ______________ Date ____________

19. A(An) ________________ is a preparation of weakened or killed pathogens.

20. Single-stranded RNA molecules that have no surrounding capsids and infect plants are called ________________ .

Short Answer

In complete sentences, write the answers to the questions on the lines provided.

21. Identify structures A through D in Figure 1.

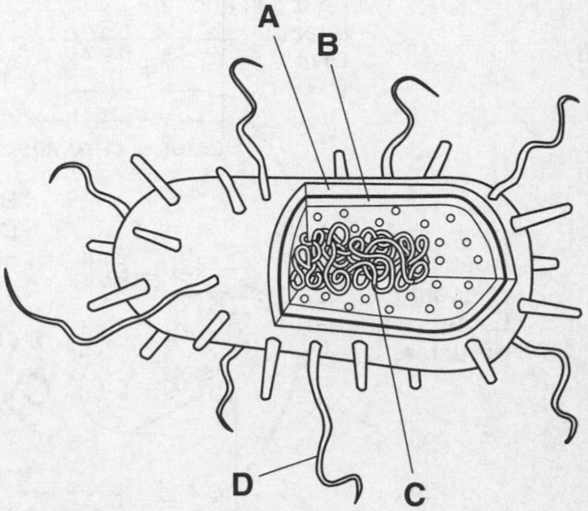

Figure 1

22. Name the two kingdoms of prokaryotes. List one way that these two groups differ from each other.

23. What is a pathogen?

24. What are two general ways that bacteria produce disease?

25. What are three methods used to control bacterial growth?

Name_____ Class_____ Date _____

Using Science Skills

Use the diagram below to answer the following questions on the lines provided.

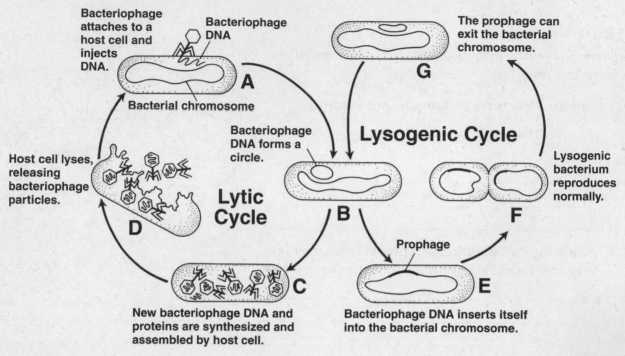

Figure 2

26. **Interpreting Graphics** What does Figure 2 represent?

_____

_____

27. **Comparing and Contrasting** Look at both cycles shown in Figure 2. During which cycle is the host cell destroyed?

_____

28. **Interpreting Graphics** Each stage of the cycles shown in Figure 2 is labeled with a letter. Which letter indicates the stage at which the bacteriophage's DNA becomes a part of the host cell's DNA?

_____

29. **Interpreting Graphics** Which letter in Figure 2 indicates the stage at which a host cell begins producing new bacteriophages?

_____

30. **Interpreting Graphics** Which letter in Figure 2 indicates the stage at which a bacteriophage injects its DNA into a host cell?

_____

LESSON PLAN 20–1 (pages 497–498)

Time
1 periods
1/2 block

The Kingdom Protista

Section Objective   **Local Standards**

■ **20.1.1 Explain** what a protist is.

Vocabulary protist

1 FOCUS

Vocabulary Preview

Ask students to propose a definition for the word *protist* before they read the section.

Targeted Resources

❑ Transparencies: **295** Section 20–1 Interest Grabber

❑ Transparencies: **296** Section 20–1 Outline

❑ Transparencies: **297** Concept Map

2 INSTRUCT

Build Science Skills: Observing

Students make slides of samples from pond water and observe protists through a microscope. **L2** **L3**

Make Connections: Earth Science

Review basic events of Earth's history, from Earth's formation to the Cambrian Explosion at the beginning of the Paleozoic Era. **L2**

Build Science Skills: Classifying

Students observe a variety of protists and create their own classification system. **L2**

Targeted Resources

❑ Reading and Study Workbook: Section 20–1

❑ Adapted Reading and Study Workbook: Section 20–1

❑ Teaching Resources: Section Summaries 20–1, Worksheets 20–1

❑ **NSTA** *sciLINKS* Protists

3 ASSESS

Evaluate Understanding

Have students explain the classification of protists based on nutrition.

Reteach

Ask students to explain why none of the organisms in Figure 20–1 could be classified as an animal or a fungus.

Targeted Resources

❑ Teaching Resources: Section Review 20–1

❑ *i*Text Section 20–1

LESSON PLAN 20–2 (pages 499–505)

Animal-like Protists: Protozoans

Time
2 periods
1 block

Section Objectives

Local Standards

■ **20.2.1 Describe** the major phyla of animal-like protists.

■ **20.2.2 Explain** how animal-like protists harm other living things.

Vocabulary pseudopod • amoeboid movement • food vacuole • cilium • trichocyst • macronucleus • micronucleus • gullet • anal pore • contractile vacuole • conjugation

1 FOCUS

Reading Strategy
Students copy the key concepts on a notecard and add supporting details as they read.

Targeted Resources
❑ Transparencies: **298** Section 20–2 Interest Grabber

❑ Transparencies: **299** Section 20–2 Outline

2 INSTRUCT

Build Science Skills: Observing
Students gather grass, prepare it for slide making, and then observe different types of paramecia with a microscope. **L2 L3**

Use Visuals: Figure 20–5
Use Figure 20–5 to review characteristics of ciliates. **L1 L2**

Build Science Skills: Comparing and Contrasting
Students make a table to organize information about the four phyla of protozoans. **L2**

Make Connections: Health Science
Review the geography of malarial infection and the basics of the treatment and prevention of malaria. **L1 L2**

Quick Lab
Students observe paramecia and formulate a hypothesis about how paramecia feed. **L2 L3**

Targeted Resources
❑ Reading and Study Workbook: Section 20–2

❑ Adapted Reading and Study Workbook: Section 20–2

❑ Teaching Resources: Section Summaries 20–2, Worksheets 20–2

❑ Transparencies: **300** Conjugation, **301** Figure 20–4 An Amoeba, **302** Figure 20–5 A Ciliate, **303** Figure 20–7 The Life Cycle of *Plasmodium*

❑ Lab Worksheets: Chapter 20 Design an Experiment

❑ Lab Manual B: Chapter 20 Lab

❑ **PHSchool.com** Protozoans

3 ASSESS

Evaluate Understanding
Have students write a paragraph that compares an amoeba to a paramecium.

Reteach
Students make a concept map that organizes information about animallike protists.

Targeted Resources
❑ Teaching Resources: Section Review 20–2

❑ **ⓘText** Section 20–2

LESSON PLAN 20–3 (pages 506–509)

Plantlike Protists: Unicellular Algae

Time
2 periods
1 block

Section Objectives

- **20.3.1 Describe** the function of chlorophyll and accessory pigments in algae.
- **20.3.2 Describe** the major phyla of unicellular algae.
- **20.3.3 Summarize** the ecological roles of unicellular algae.

Vocabulary accessory pigment • eyespot • pellicle
• phytoplankton

Local Standards

---

1 FOCUS

Vocabulary Preview
Have students skim the section for boldface Vocabulary words and write down their definitions.

Targeted Resources
❏ Transparencies: **304** Section 20–3 Interest Grabber
❏ Transparencies: **305** Section 20–3 Outline

---

2 INSTRUCT

Demonstration
Boil samples of red, brown, and green algae in alcohol and allow students to compare pigments from each on filter paper. **L2**

Build Science Skills: Observing
Challenge students to use a microscope to find structures on a prepared slide of euglena, like those shown in Figure 20–10. **L2 L3**

Use Visuals: Figure 20–12
Use Figure 20–12 to review the characteristics of dinoflagellates. **L1 L2**

Analyzing Data
Students analyze data in a graph and draw conclusions about the effect of fertilizers on the growth of algae. **L2**

Use Visuals: Figure 20–13
Use Figure 20–13 to reinforce an understanding of the causes of red tides. **L2**

Targeted Resources
❏ Reading and Study Workbook: Section 20–3
❏ Adapted Reading and Study Workbook: Section 20–3
❏ Transparencies: **306** Euglena
❏ Teaching Resources: Section Summaries 20–3, Worksheets 20–3, Enrichment

---

3 ASSESS

Evaluate Understanding
Call on students to provide details about each of the four phyla discussed in the section.

Reteach
Have students compare the euglena in Figure 20–10 with the paramecium in Figure 20–5.

Targeted Resources
❏ Teaching Resources: Section Review 20–3
❏ *i* **Text** Section 20–3

LESSON PLAN 20–4 (pages 510–515)

Plantlike Protists: Red, Brown, and Green Algae

Section Objectives   **Local Standards**

■ **20.4.1 Describe** the major phyla of multicellular algae.

■ **20.4.2 Explain** how multicellular algae reproduce.

■ **20.4.3 Identify** some human uses of algae.

Vocabulary phycobilin • filament • alternation of generations • gametophyte • spore • sporophyte

1 FOCUS

Reading Strategy
Students make an outline of the section by using the blue and the green headings and then add details as they read.

Targeted Resources
❏ Transparencies: **307** Section 20–4 Interest Grabber

❏ Transparencies: **308** Section 20–4 Outline

2 INSTRUCT

Make Connections: Physics
Introduce the function of pigments by reviewing the reflection and absorption of light and what causes color. **L1** **L2**

Build Science Skills: Classifying
Students examine and classify an alga, a fern, a plant, and a moss. **L2**

Build Science Skills: Comparing and Contrasting
Students make microscope slides of green algae and observe the slides through a microscope. **L2** **L3**

Use Visuals: Figure 20–17
Use Figure 20–17 to reinforce an understanding of reproduction in green algae. **L2**

Use Visuals: Figure 20–18
Use Figure 20–18 to reinforce an understanding of reproduction in green algae. **L2**

Targeted Resources
❏ Reading and Study Workbook: Section 20–4

❏ Adapted Reading and Study Workbook: Section 20–4

❏ Teaching Resources: Section Summaries 20–4, Worksheets 20–4

❏ Transparencies: **309** *Ulva* Life Cycle, **310** Figure 20–17 The Life Cycle of *Chlamydomonas*

❏ **NSTA** *sci*LINKS Algae

3 ASSESS

Evaluate Understanding
Students make a table to organize information about the three phyla of protists discussed.

Reteach
Students make their own drawings of the life cycle of *Ulva*, using Figure 20–18 as a model.

Targeted Resources
❏ Teaching Resources: Section Review 20–4

❏ **iText** Section 20–4

LESSON PLAN 20–5 (pages 516–520)

Time
1 period
1/2 block

Funguslike Protists

Section Objectives

- **20.5.1 Compare and Contrast** funguslike protists and fungi.
- **20.5.2 Describe** slime molds and water molds.
- **20.5.3 Summarize** the ecological roles of funguslike protists.

Vocabulary cellular slime mold • acellular slime mold • fruiting body • plasmodium • hypha • zoosporangium • antheridium • oogonium

Local Standards

1 FOCUS

Reading Strategy
Students rewrite the blue headings as *how, why,* or *what* questions and then answer their questions as they read the section.

Targeted Resources
❑ Transparencies: **311** Section 20–5 Interest Grabber
❑ Transparencies: **312** Section 20–5 Outline

2 INSTRUCT

Use Visuals: Figure 20–22
Use Figure 20–22 to review the life cycle of cellular slime molds. **L2**

Demonstration
Have students observe the growth of an acellular slime mold plasmodium. **L1 L2**

Demonstration
Have students observe the growth of water mold on a dead fish. **L1 L2**

Make Connections: Environmental Science
Focus attention on the role that funguslike protists play in the environment. **L1 L2**

Targeted Resources
❑ Reading and Study Workbook: Section 20–5
❑ Adapted Reading and Study Workbook: Section 20–5
❑ Teaching Resources: Section Summaries 20–5, Worksheets 20–5
❑ Transparencies: **313** The Life Cycle of a Water Mold, **314** Figure 20–22 The Life Cycle of a Cellular Slime Mold, **315** Figure 20–23 The Life Cycle of an Acellular Slime Mold
❑ Lab Manual A: Chapter 20 Lab
❑ **PHSchool.com** Funguslike protists

3 ASSESS

Evaluate Understanding
Call on students to compare and contrast the two types of slime molds.

Reteach
Have students explain the processes illustrated in Figure 20–23.

Targeted Resources
❑ Teaching Resources: Section Review 20–5, Chapter Vocabulary Review, Graphic Organizer, Chapter 20 Tests: Levels A and B
❑ *iText* Section 20–5, Chapter 20 Assessment
❑ **PHSchool.com** Online Chapter 20 Test

Chapter 20   Protists

Summary

20–1 The Kingdom Protista

The kingdom Protista is a diverse group. **Protists are eukaryotes that are not members of the kingdoms Plantae, Animalia, or Fungi.** Most protists are unicellular. Earth's first eukaryotes were protists. One way protists are classified is according to how they obtain nutrition. Thus, many protists that are heterotrophic are called animal-like protists. Protists that produce their own food by photosynthesis are called plantlike protists. Protists that obtain their food by external digestion are called funguslike protists.

20–2 Animal-like Protists: Protozoans

Animal-like protists are called protozoans. Protozoans are heterotrophs. There are four phyla of animal-like protists. They are classified according to how they move.

- **Protists that swim using flagella are classified in the phylum Zoomastigina.** They are called zooflagellates. Flagella are long, whiplike projections that allow a cell to move.
- **Members of the phylum Sarcodina move by using pseudopods. Sarcodines also use pseudopods for feeding. Pseudopods** are temporary projections of cytoplasm. Sarcodines called amoebas have thick pseudopods. An ameoba moves by first extending its psuedopod. The cell's cytoplasm flows into the pseudopod. The rest of the cell then follows. This type of movement is called **amoeboid movement.**
- **Members of the phylum Ciliophora, known as ciliates, use cilia for feeding and movement. Cilia** are short, hairlike projections similar to flagella. Some of the best-known ciliates belong to the genus *Paramecium*. The cilia of a paramecium are organized into evenly spaced rows and bundles. Just under the cell membrane, a paramecium has small defense structures called **trichocysts.** When a paramecium is in danger, the trichocysts release stiff projections that protect the cell.
- **Members of the phylum Sporozoa do not move on their own. They are parasites that reproduce by means of sporozoites.**

Some animal-like protists cause serious diseases. For example, *Plasmodium* is a sporozoan that causes malaria. *Trypanosoma* is a zooflagellate. It causes African sleeping sickness.

Some animal-like protists are helpful. *Trichonympha* lives in the digestive system of termites. This protist helps termites digest wood.

20–3 Plantlike Protists: Unicellular Algae

Plantlike protists are called algae. One of the key traits used to classify algae is the photosynthetic **pigments** they contain. **Chlorophyll and accessory pigments allow algae to harvest and use the energy from sunlight.** Unicellular plantlike protists include four phyla.

- **Euglenophytes have two flagella and no cell wall.** Euglenophytes have chloroplasts, but in most other ways they are like zooflagellates. The phylum gets its name from the genus *Euglena.* To move, a euglena spins the longer of its two flagella. This pulls the euglena through the water.
- **Chrysophytes are a diverse group of plantlike protists that have gold-colored chloroplasts.**
- **Diatoms produce thin, delicate cell walls rich in silicon (Si).**
- Dinoflagellates generally have two flagella. **About half of the dinoflagellates are photosynthetic. The other half live as heterotrophs.**

Plantlike protists are ecologically important. They make up much of phytoplankton. Phytoplankton are small photosynthetic organisms that float near the ocean's surface.

Many protists grow quickly in places where sewage is dumped into water. When the amount of waste is excessive, algae grow into huge masses called algal blooms.

20–4 Plantlike Protists: Red, Brown, and Green Algae

Three phyla of plantlike protists include mostly multicellular organisms. They are grouped by their photosynthetic pigments.

- Red algae are members of phylum Rhodophyta. **These algae can live at great depths because of their ability to harvest light energy. They contain chlorophyll *a* and reddish accessory pigments called phycobilins.**
- Brown algae are members of the phylum Phaeophyta. **They contain chlorophyll *a* and *c* and a brown accessory pigment.** The largest alga is giant kelp, a brown alga that grows to more than 60 meters long.
- Green algae, which share many characteristics with plants, are members of the phylum Chlorophyta. **Both plants and green algae have the same photosynthetic pigments, chlorophyll *a* and *b*.** Scientists hypothesize that the ancestors of modern land plants looked like green algae. Several species of green algae live in multicellular colonies.

Many algae life cycles include both a diploid and a haploid stage. The process of switching back and forth between haploid and diploid stages in a life cycle is called **alternation of generations.**

Algae produce much of Earth's oxygen through photosynthesis. Algae are a major food source for animals and people. Industry uses algae in making plastics and other products.

20–5 Funguslike Protists

Like fungi, funguslike protists are heterotrophs that absorb food from dead or decaying organic matter. Unlike most fungi, though, funguslike protists have centrioles. They also lack the chitin cell walls of fungi.

Slime molds are funguslike protists that play key roles in recycling organic matter. At one stage of their life cycle, slime molds look like amoebas. At other stages, they form moldlike clumps that produce spores. There are two kinds of slime molds.

- In **cellular slime molds,** individual cells remain distinct during every phase of the life cycle. They spend most of their lives as free-living cells.
- In **acellular slime molds,** cells fuse to form large cells with many nuclei. These structures are known as plasmodia. **Fruiting bodies,** or sporangia, spring up from a plasmodium.

Water molds, or oomycetes, are members of the phylum Oomycota. **Oomycetes thrive on dead or decaying organic matter in water. Some oomycetes are plant parasites on land.**

Slime molds and water molds are important recyclers of organic material. Some funguslike protists can cause diseases in plants. An oomycete caused a disease in the Irish potato crop in 1845 and 1846, leading to mass starvation.

Paramecium

A paramecium is an animal-like protist called a ciliate. It uses cilia for feeding and movement.

Label the cilia. *Then, color the structures of the paramecium.*
- Color the structures used for defense orange.
- Color the structures that contain genetic information yellow.
- Color the structures that eliminate waste materials, including excess water, green.

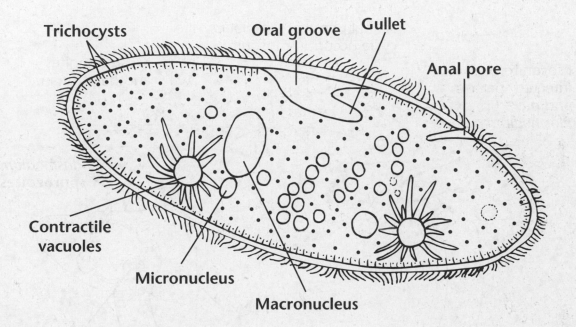

Answer the questions.

1. What is a trichocyst?

   _____

   _____

2. Which structure helps maintain homeostasis by removing excess water? Circle the correct answer.

   contractile vacuole   gullet

Protists as Parasites

Some animal-like protists are parasites that cause serious diseases in humans and other animals. The life cycle of the sporozoan *Plasmodium* is diagrammed below.

Follow the prompts.

- Circle the stage in which a mosquito becomes infected with the protist.
- Place an X on the stage in which a human becomes infected with the protist.

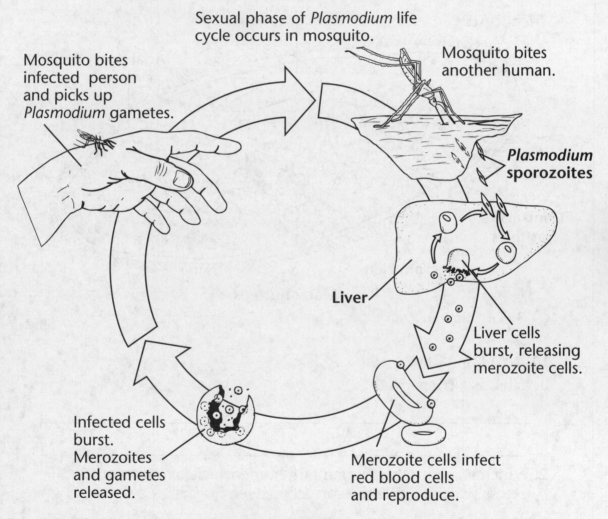

Sexual phase of *Plasmodium* life cycle occurs in mosquito.

Mosquito bites infected person and picks up *Plasmodium* gametes.

Mosquito bites another human.

***Plasmodium* sporozoites**

Liver

Liver cells burst, releasing merozoite cells.

Infected cells burst. Merozoites and gametes released.

Merozoite cells infect red blood cells and reproduce.

Use the diagram to answer the questions.

1. Which type of human cell releases *Plasmodium* gametes when it bursts? Circle the correct answer.

   liver cells   red blood cells

2. What disease does *Plasmodium* cause?

   _____

Euglena

The euglena is a plantlike protist. It has two flagella but no cell wall.
Label the flagella, chloroplast *and* eyespot *on the diagram.*

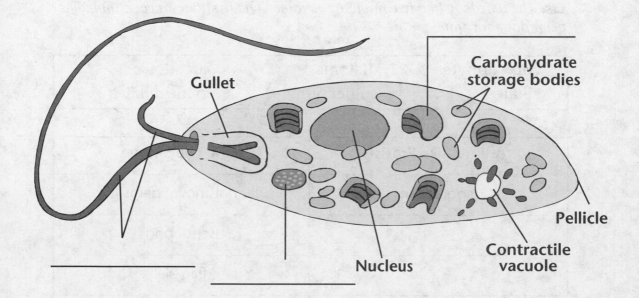

Gullet

Carbohydrate
storage bodies

Pellicle

Contractile
vacuole

Nucleus

_____

_____

Write the function of each of the structures on the lines provided.

Flagella _____

Chloroplast _____

Eyespot _____

Use the diagram to answer the questions.

 1. How are euglenas similar to animal-like zooflagellates?

_____

_____

 2. Why are euglenas classified as plantlike protists?

_____

_____

Protist Characteristics

Animal-like protists are divided into four groups according to the way they move. Unicellular plantlike protists are divided into four groups according to various cellular characteristics.

Use the words below to complete the table. The first one in each table has been done for you.

chrysophytes	diatoms	sarcodines
ciliates	euglenophytes	zooflagellates

Animal-like Protists	How They Move
sporozoans	do not move; parasitic
	pseudopods
	flagella
	cilia

Plantlike Protists	Identifying Characteristics(s)
dinoflagellates	some photosynthetic, some heterotrophs; generally have flagella
	two flagella; no cell wall
	gold-colored chloroplasts
	cell walls rich in silicon

Use the tables to answer the following questions. Circle the correct answer.

1. A paramecium uses cilia to swim through the water. What type of protist is it?

sarcodine   ciliate

2. What cell structures do both zooflagellates and euglenophytes have?

chloroplasts   flagella

Algae Life Cycle

Recall that a *haploid* cell contains only a single set of chromosomes. A *diploid* cell contains two sets of chromosomes. Many algae switch back and forth between haploid and diploid stages during their life cycles. This process is called alternation of generations.

Color the arrows representing haploid phases of the algae life cycle yellow. Color the arrows representing diploid phases blue.

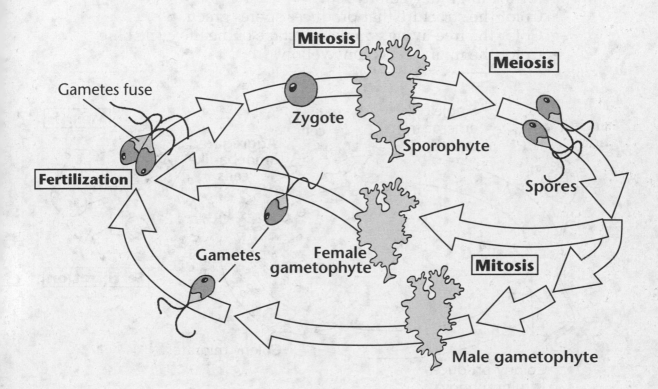

Use the diagram to answer the questions.

1. What does a sporophyte produce?

_____

2. What does a gametophyte produce?

_____

3. What forms when gametes fuse?

_____

Cellular Slime Molds

Cellular slime molds spend most of their lives as single, free-living cells. When their food supply runs low, they aggregate, or come together. This aggregate of cells functions like a single organism. The life cycle of a cellular slime mold is diagrammed below.

Color the life cycle according to the prompts below.
- Color the stage that shows single cells coming together to form a migrating colony red.
- Color the structure that produces spores green.
- Color the free-living, single-cell stage of the life cycle blue.
- Color the migrating colony yellow.

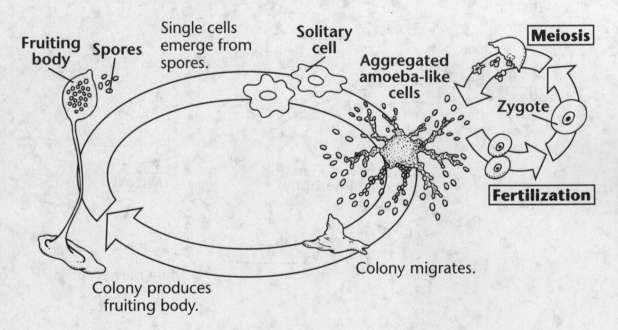

Fruiting body   Spores   Single cells emerge from spores.   Solitary cell   Aggregated amoeba-like cells   **Meiosis**   Zygote   **Fertilization**   Colony migrates.

Colony produces fruiting body.

Answer the questions. Circle the correct answer.

1. What type of protists are cellular slime molds?

plantlike   funguslike

2. What does the fruiting body produce?

spores   zygotes

Chapter 20 Protists

Vocabulary Review

Multiple Choice *In the space provided, write the letter of the term that best completes each sentence.*

_____1. Small photosynthetic organisms living near the ocean surface are called
  a. cilia.   **c.** phytoplankton.
  b. plasmodia.

_____2. The life cycle of many types of algae switches back and forth between a haploid and diploid stage through a process called
  a. amoeboid movement.   **c.** alternation of generations.
  b. conjugation.

_____3. The single structure with many nuclei that is formed by an acellular slime mold is a
  a. plasmodium.   **c.** zoosporangium.
  b. cilium.

_____4. Amoebas move and feed by using their
  a. pseudopods.   **c.** eyespots.
  b. oogonium.

_____5. An organism that is not a prokaryote, a plant, an animal, or a fungus is a
  a. phycobilin.   **c.** gullet.
  b. protist.

_____6. Some ciliates can exchange genetic material with other individuals through a reproductive process called
  a. amoeboid movement.   **c.** fruiting bodies.
  b. conjugation.

_____7. To help find sunlight, euglenas use their
  a. micronuclei.   **c.** eyespots.
  b. macronuclei.

_____8. The haploid reproductive cell made by *Ulva* that can grow into a new individual without fusing with another cell is a
  a. spore.   **c.** sporophyte.
  b. trichocyst.

_____9. A paramecium moves by using hairlike projections called
  a. gametophytes.   **c.** cilia.
  b. contractile vacuoles.

Summary

20–1 The Kingdom Protista

The kingdom Protista is a diverse group. Protists are eukaryotes that are not members of the kingdoms Plantae, Animalia, or Fungi. Most protists are unicellular. The first eukaryotic organisms on Earth were protists.

Protists, which first appeared about 1.5 billion years ago, were the first group of eukaryotes to evolve. One explanation for the way the first eukaryotes developed from prokaryotes has been credited to Lynn Margulis. Margulis's hypothesis states that the first eukaryote—and the first protist—was formed by a symbiosis among several prokaryotes. Evidence to support this hypothesis includes structural similarities between certain eukaryotic organelles and bacteria.

Because protists are such a diverse group, scientists don't always agree on how to classify them. One way to classify protists is according to the way they obtain nutrition. There are animal-like protists, plantlike protists, and funguslike protists.

20–2 Animal-like Protists: Protozoans

Animal-like protists—also called protozoans—are heterotrophs. The four phyla of animal-like protists are classified according to the way they move.

Animal-like protists that swim using flagella are classified in the phylum Zoomastigina. They are called zooflagellates. Members of the phylum Sarcodina move by means of temporary projections of cytoplasm known as pseudopods. Sarcodines use pseudopods for feeding and movement. Sarcodines called amoebas have thick pseudopods. The phylum Ciliophora is named for cilia, which are short hairlike projections similar to flagella. Ciliates use cilia for feeding and movement. Some of the best-known ciliates belong to the genus *Paramecium*. Members of the phylum Sporozoa are parasites and do not move on their own. Sporozoans reproduce by means of sporozoites.

Some animal-like protists cause serious diseases. The sporozoan *Plasmodium* causes malaria. The zooflagellate *Trypanosoma* causes African sleeping sickness. Some animal-like protists are beneficial to organisms. *Trichonympha* lives within the digestive system of termites and helps termites digest wood.

20–3 Plantlike Protists: Unicellular Algae

Plantlike protists are commonly called algae. Plantlike protists include four phyla that contain unicellular organisms. One of the key traits used to classify algae is the photosynthetic pigments they contain. Chlorophyll includes three forms. Each form absorbs a different wavelength of light. Many algae also have compounds called accessory pigments that absorb light at different wavelengths than chlorophyll.

Euglenophytes—members of the phylum Euglenophyta—are plantlike protists that have two flagella but no cell wall. Euglenophytes have chloroplasts, but in most other ways they are like the protozoans called zooflagellates.

Chrysophytes—members of the phylum Chrysophyta—are a diverse group of plantlike protists that have gold-colored chloroplasts. Diatoms—members of the phylum Bacillariophyta—produce thin, delicate cell walls rich in silicon. Silicon (Si) is the main component of glass. These walls are shaped like a petri dish or a flat pillbox.

Dinoflagellates—members of the phylum Pyrrophyta—generally have two flagella. About half of the dinoflagellates are photosynthetic. The other half live as heterotrophs.

Plantlike protists play a major ecological role on Earth by being a considerable part of the phytoplankton. Phytoplankton are made up of the population of small photosynthetic organisms found near the surface of the ocean. Many protists grow rapidly in regions where sewage is dumped into water. When the amount of waste is excessive, algae grow into enormous masses called algal blooms.

20–4 Plantlike Protists: Red, Brown, and Green Algae

Three phyla of plantlike protists contain mostly multicellular organisms. The most important differences among these phyla are their photosynthetic pigments. Red algae—members of phylum Rhodophyta—are able to live at great depths due to their efficiency in harvesting light energy. Red algae contain chlorophyll *a* and reddish accessory pigments called phycobilins.

Brown algae—members of the phylum Phaeophyta—contain chlorophyll *a* and *c* as well as a brown accessory pigment called fucoxanthin. The largest alga is giant kelp, a brown alga that grows to be more than 60 meters in length.

Green algae—members of the phylum Chlorophyta—share many characteristics with plants. They share the same photosynthetic pigments, chlorophyll *a* and *b*. Both plants and green algae have cellulose in their cell walls. Also, green algae are like plants in that they store food in the form of starch. These shared characteristics lead scientists to hypothesize that the ancestors of modern land plants looked like green algae. Green algae include the unicellular *Chlamydomonas*. Several species of green algae live in multicellular colonies. *Ulva*, called "sea lettuce," is a true multicellular green alga.

The life cycles of many algae include both a diploid and a haploid generation. The process of switching back and forth between haploid stages and diploid stages in a life cycle is called alternation of generations.

Algae produce much of Earth's oxygen through photosynthesis. Algae are a major food source in the oceans. People also use algae for food. Industry uses algae in making plastics and other products.

20–5 Funguslike Protists

Funguslike protists are like fungi in that they are heterotrophs that absorb food from dead or decaying organic matter. Unlike most true fungi, though, funguslike protists have centrioles. They also lack the chitin cell walls of true fungi.

Slime molds are funguslike protists that play key roles in recycling organic material. At one stage of their life cycle, slime molds look just like amoebas. At other stages, they form moldlike clumps that produce spores, almost like fungi. In cellular slime molds, individual cells remain distinct during every phase of the life cycle. They spend most of their lives as free-living cells. In acellular slime molds, cells fuse to form large cells with many nuclei. These structures are known as plasmodia. Fruiting bodies, or sporangia, spring up from a plasmodium.

Water molds, or oomycetes, are members of the phylum Oomycota. Oomycetes thrive on dead or decaying organic matter in water. Some oomycetes are plant parasites on land.

Slime molds and water molds are important recyclers of organic material. Some funguslike protists can cause diseases in plants. An oomycete caused a disease in the Irish potato crop in 1845 and 1846, leading to mass starvation.

Section 20–1 The Kingdom Protista (pages 497–498)

🔑 Key Concept
- What are protists?

What Is a Protist? (page 497)

1. What is a protist? _____

_____

2. Circle the letter of each sentence that is true about protists.

   a. All are unicellular.

   b. All cells have a nucleus.

   c. All cells have membrane-bound organelles.

   d. All are multicellular.

3. Why are some organisms that consist of thousands of cells considered to be protists?

_____

_____

Evolution of Protists (page 498)

4. The first eukaryotic organisms on Earth were _____.

5. What is biologist Lynn Margulis's hypothesis about where the first protists came from?

_____

_____

_____

_____

Classification of Protists (page 498)

6. Complete the table about protist classification.

GROUPS OF PROTISTS

Group	Method of Obtaining Food
	Consume other organisms
Plantlike protists	
Funguslike protists	

7. What don't categories of protists based on the way they obtain food reflect about these organisms? _____

_____

Reading Skill Practice

By looking at illustrations in textbooks, you can help yourself remember better what you have read. Look carefully at Figure 20–1 on page 497. What important idea do these photographs communicate? Do your work on a separate sheet of paper.

Section 20–2 Animal-like Protists: Protozoans
(pages 499–505)

🔑 **Key Concepts**
- What are the distinguishing features of the major phyla of animal-like protists?
- How do animal-like protists harm other living things?

Introduction (page 499)

1. At one time, what were all animal-like protists called? _____

2. How are the four phyla of animal-like protists distinguished from one another?
_____
_____

Zooflagellates (page 499)

3. What kind of protists are classified in the phylum Zoomastigina? _____
_____

4. How many flagella does a zooflagellate have? _____
_____

5. Zooflagellates reproduce asexually by means of _____.

6. Is the following sentence true or false? Some zooflagellates have a sexual life cycle.
_____

Sarcodines (page 500)

7. Sarcodines are members of the phylum _____.

8. What are pseudopods? _____
_____

9. What do sarcodines use pseudopods for? _____
_____

10. What is amoeboid movement? _____
_____

11. What is a food vacuole? _____
_____

12. How do amoebas capture and digest food? _____
_____
_____

13. Amoebas reproduce by means of _____.

Ciliates (pages 501–502)

14. Ciliates are members of the phylum _____.

15. What are cilia? _____

16. What do ciliates use cilia for? _____

Match the ciliate structure with its description.

Structure	Description
_____ **17.** Trichocysts	**a.** Indentation on one side of a ciliate into which food is swept
_____ **18.** Macronucleus	**b.** Smaller nucleus containing a "reserve copy" of the cell's genes
_____ **19.** Micronucleus	**c.** Small, bottle-shaped structures used for defense
_____ **20.** Gullet	**d.** Region of cell membrane where waste-containing food vacuoles fuse
_____ **21.** Anal pore	**e.** Larger nucleus containing multiple copies of most of the cell's genes
_____ **22.** Contractile vacuole	**f.** Cavity in cytoplasm specialized to collect and pump out water

23. Label the illustration of a paramecium.

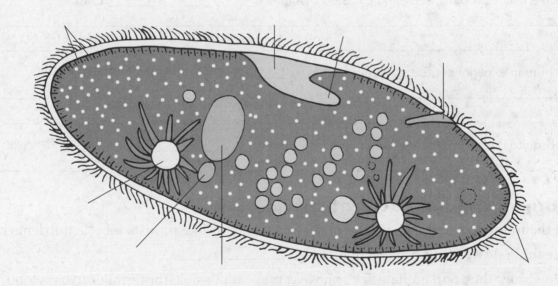

24. What is conjugation? _____

_____

25. Within a large population, how does conjugation benefit ciliates? _____

_____

Sporozoans (page 502)

26. Sporozoans are members of the phylum _____.

27. Circle the letter of each sentence that is true about sporozoans.

   a. They are parasitic.   c. All have only one host.

   b. They do not move on their own.   d. They reproduce by means of sporozoites.

Animal-like Protists and Disease (pages 503–504)

28. What causes malaria? _____
_____

29. Complete the flowchart about the cycle of malarial infection.

An infected *Anopheles* mosquito bites a human and deposits *Plasmodium* spores into the

_____.

↓

The spores travel to the _____.

↓

Infected liver cells burst, releasing parasites that infect _____ cells.

↓

The human experiences the symptoms of _____.

↓

A mosquito bites the infected human and picks up the _____ cells.

Ecology of Animal-like Protists (page 505)

30. Is the following sentence true or false? Some animal-like protists recycle nutrients by breaking down dead organic matter. _____

31. How does the zooflagellate *Trichonympha* make it possible for termites to eat wood?

_____

_____

_____

_____

_____

Section 20–3 Plantlike Protists: Unicellular Algae (pages 506–509)

⟅⟆ Key Concepts
- What is the function of chlorophyll and accessory pigments in algae?
- What are the distinguishing features of the major phyla of unicellular algae?

Introduction (page 506)

1. Plantlike protists are commonly called _____.

2. Is the following sentence true or false? Algae include only multicellular organisms.

_____

Chlorophyll and Accessory Pigments (page 506)

3. In the process of photosynthesis, what substances trap the energy of sunlight?

_____

_____

4. How does water affect the sunlight that passes through it? _____

_____

5. Why does the dim blue light that penetrates deep into the sea contain little energy that

chlorophyll *a* can use? _____

_____

6. How have various groups of algae adapted to conditions of limited light?

_____

_____

7. What are accessory pigments? _____

_____

8. Why are algae such a wide range of colors? _____

_____

Euglenophytes (page 507)

9. Euglenophytes are members of the phylum _____.

10. Circle the letter of each sentence that is true about euglenophytes.

   a. They are remarkably similar to zooflagellates.

   b. They possess chloroplasts.

   c. They have a cell wall.

   d. They have two flagella.

Name_____ Class_____ Date_____

11. What is an eyespot, and what is its function? _____
_____
_____

12. Euglenas have a tough, intricate membrane called a(an) _____.

13. How do euglenas reproduce? _____

14. Label the illustration of a euglena.

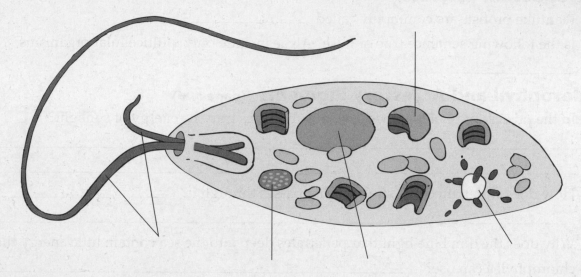

Chrysophytes (page 507)

15. The yellow-green algae and the golden-brown algae are members of the phylum
_____.

16. What color are the chloroplasts of chrysophytes? _____

17. Circle the letter of each sentence that is true about chrysophytes.

    a. The cell walls of some contain the carbohydrate pectin.

    b. They reproduce sexually but not asexually.

    c. They generally store food in the form of oil.

    d. Some form threadlike colonies.

Diatoms (page 507)

18. Diatoms are members of the phylum _____.

19. Circle the letter of each sentence that is true about diatoms.

    a. They are very rare in almost all environments.

    b. Their cell walls are rich in silicon.

    c. They are shaped like a petri dish or flat pillbox.

    d. They are among the most abundant organisms on Earth.

Dinoflagellates (page 508)

20. Dinoflagellates are members of the phylum _____.

21. How do dinoflagellates obtain nutrition? _____
_____
_____

22. Circle the letter of each sentence that is true about dinoflagellates.

    a. They generally have one flagellum.

    b. Many species are luminescent.

    c. Most reproduce by binary fission.

Ecology of Unicellular Algae (pages 508–509)

23. How do plantlike protists make much of the diversity of aquatic life possible?
_____

24. What are phytoplankton? _____
_____

25. What are algal blooms? _____
_____

26. How can an algal bloom be harmful? _____
_____
_____
_____

Section 20–4 Plantlike Protists: Red, Brown, and Green Algae (pages 510–515)

Key Concepts
- What are the distinguishing features of the major phyla of multicellular algae?
- How do multicellular algae reproduce?

Introduction (page 510)

1. What are seaweeds? _____

2. What are the most important differences among the three phyla of multicellular algae?
_____
_____

Red Algae (page 510)

3. Red algae are members of the phylum _____.

4. Why are red algae able to live at great depths? _____
_____

5. What pigments do red algae contain? _____
_____

6. Which color of light are phycobilins especially good at absorbing?

   a. red   **b.** green   **c.** yellow   **d.** blue

7. Circle the letter of each sentence that is true about red algae.

   a. They can grow in the ocean at depths up to 260 meters.

   b. Most are unicellular.

   c. All are red or reddish-brown.

   d. Coralline algae play an important role in coral reef formation.

Brown Algae (page 511)

8. Brown algae are members of the phylum _____.

9. What pigments do brown algae contain? _____
_____

Match each structure with its description.

	Structure	Description
_____	10. Holdfast	**a.** Flattened stemlike structure
_____	11. Stipe	**b.** Gas-filled swelling
_____	12. Blade	**c.** Structure that attaches alga to the bottom
_____	13. Bladder	**d.** Leaflike structure

14. Where are brown algae commonly found growing? _____

_____

15. What is the largest known alga? _____

Green Algae (pages 511–512)

16. Green algae are members of the phylum _____.

17. What characteristics do green algae share with plants? _____

_____

18. What do scientists think is the connection between mosses and green algae?

_____

19. The freshwater alga *Spirogyra* forms long threadlike colonies called

_____.

20. How can the cells in a *Volvox* colony coordinate movement? _____

_____

21. "Sea lettuce" is a multicellular alga known as _____.

Reproduction in Green Algae (pages 512–514)

22. What occurs in the process known as alternation of generations? _____

_____

_____

23. The unicellular *Chlamydomonas* reproduces asexually by producing

_____.

24. Circle the letter of each sentence that is true about sexual reproduction in
Chlamydomonas.

   a. If conditions become unfavorable, cells release gametes.

   b. Paired gametes form a diploid zygote.

   c. A zygote quickly grows into an adult organism.

   d. The gametes are called male and female.

25. Complete the table about the generations in an organism's life cycle.

GENERATIONS IN A LIFE CYCLE

Generation	Definition	Diploid or Haploid?
	Gamete-producing phase	
	Spore-producing phase	

26. Complete the life cycle of *Ulva* by labeling the sporophyte, the male gametophyte, and the female gametophyte. Also, label the places where the processes of fertilization, mitosis, and meiosis occur.

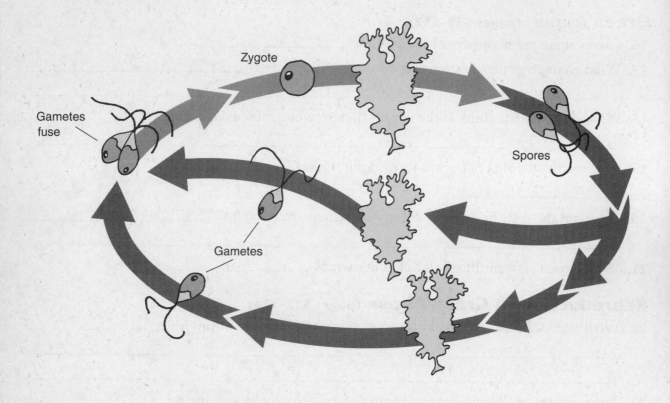

Ecology of Algae (page 515)

27. Why have algae been called the "grasses" of the sea? _____

_____

28. Through photosynthesis, algae produce much of Earth's _____.

29. What is the compound agar derived from, and how is it used? _____

_____

_____

_____

Section 20–5 Funguslike Protists (pages 516–520)

🔑 Key Concepts
- What are the similarities and differences between funguslike protists and fungi?
- What are the defining characteristics of the slime molds and water molds?

Introduction (page 516)

1. How are funguslike protists like fungi? _____
_____
_____

2. How are funguslike protists unlike most true fungi? _____
_____

Slime Molds (pages 516–518)

3. What are slime molds? _____
_____

4. Cellular slime molds belong to the phylum _____.

5. Is the following sentence true or false? Cellular slime molds spend most of their lives as free-living cells. _____

6. What do cellular slime molds form when their food supply is exhausted? _____
_____
_____

7. What structure does a cellular slime mold colony produce, and what is that structure's function? _____
_____
_____

8. Acellular slime molds belong to the phylum _____.

9. What is a plasmodium? _____
_____
_____

10. The plasmodium eventually produces sporangia, which in turn produce haploid _____.

Water Molds (pages 518–519)

11. Water molds, or oomycetes, are members of the phylum _____.

12. Water molds produce thin filaments known as _____.

13. What are zoosporangia? _____

_____

_____

14. Where are male and female nuclei produced in water mold sexual reproduction?

_____

_____

_____

15. Fertilization in water molds occurs in the _____.

Ecology of Funguslike Protists (page 519)

16. Why aren't there bodies of dead animals and plants littering the woods and fields you
walk through? _____

_____

_____

17. What are examples of plant diseases that water molds cause? _____

_____

Water Molds and the Potato Famine (page 520)

18. What produced the Great Potato Famine of 1846? _____

_____

_____

19. What did the Great Potato Famine lead to? _____

_____

_____

Vocabulary Review

Matching   *In the space provided, write the letter of the description that best matches each organism.*

_____ **1.** sarcodines

_____ **2.** ciliates

_____ **3.** euglenophytes

_____ **4.** diatoms

_____ **5.** brown algae

_____ **6.** green algae

_____ **7.** slime molds

_____ **8.** water molds

a. unicellular algae that produce thin, delicate cell walls rich in silicon

b. funguslike protists that look just like amoebas at one stage of their life cycles

c. plantlike protists that share many characteristics with plants

d. protozoans that use pseudopods for feeding and movement

e. funguslike protists that thrive on dead or decaying organic matter in water

f. unicellular algae that have two flagella but no cell wall

g. protozoans that include those belonging to the genus *Paramecium*

h. multicellular algae that contain fucoxanthin

Completion   *Fill in the blanks with terms from Chapter 20.*

 9. Any organism that is not a plant, an animal, a fungus, or a prokaryote is a(an)

 _____.

10. A temporary cytoplasmic projection used in feeding and movement is called a(an)

 _____.

11. The disease _____ is caused by the sporozoan *Plasmodium.*

12. Many algae have compounds called _____ pigments that absorb light at different wavelengths than chlorophyll.

13. _____ are the population of small, photosynthetic organisms found near the surface of the ocean.

14. The process of switching back and forth between haploid and diploid stages in a life cycle is known as _____ of generations.

15. The single structure with many nuclei produced by an acellular slime mold is called a(an) _____.

Reviewing Key Concepts

Short Answer *On the lines provided, answer the following questions.*

1. What are protists?

   _____

   _____

2. Why is it easier to define protists by what they are not, rather than by what they are?

   _____

   _____

Completion *On the lines provided, complete the following sentences.*

3. *Protista* comes from Greek words meaning _____.

4. One way to classify protists is according to the way they _____.

5. Protists that are heterotrophs are called _____.

6. Protists that produce their own food are called _____.

7. Funguslike protists obtain their food by _____.

Reviewing Key Skills

8. **Applying Concepts** Describe the proposed relationship between prokaryotes and the organelles in eukaryotes.

   _____

   _____

   _____

   _____

9. **Evaluating** Discuss how protists are categorized. Why are these categories debatable and how might analyzing the DNA change the classification system?

   _____

   _____

   _____

   _____

10. **Applying Concepts** Use your knowledge of the Greek origins of the word *protist* to determine a possible meaning for the term *protogalaxy*.

   _____

   _____

   _____

   _____

Chapter 20 Protists   **Section Review 20-2**

Reviewing Key Concepts

Identification *On the lines provided, identify each characteristic as describing either* zooflagellates, sarcodines, ciliates, *or* sporozoans.

_____ 1. use flagella to move

_____ 2. are parasitic and do not move

_____ 3. possess two nuclei: a macronucleus and a micronucleus

_____ 4. use pseudopods for feeding and movement

_____ 5. use short hairlike projections for movement

Short Answer *On the lines provided, answer the following questions.*

6. How are the four phyla of animal-like protists distinguished from one another?

_____

_____

7. Why are some protists harmful to living organisms?

_____

_____

Reviewing Key Skills

8. **Comparing and Contrasting** How are flagella and cilia similar? How are they different?

_____

_____

_____

9. **Applying Concepts** What is conjugation and how is it advantageous to a paramecium?

_____

_____

10. **Applying Concepts** Describe a situation in which an animal-like protist benefits an organism.

_____

_____

Classifying *On the lines provided, classify each picture as either a* zooflagellate, sarcodine, ciliate, *or* sporozoan.

11. Amoeba    12. Paramecium

11. _____

12. _____

Reviewing Key Concepts

Short Answer *On the lines provided, answer the following questions.*

1. In algae, what purpose do chlorophyll and accessory pigments serve?

   _____

   _____

   _____

2. What are three distinguishing features of euglenophytes?

   _____

   _____

   _____

3. How do dinoflagellates obtain nutrition?

   _____

   _____

Completion *In the spaces provided, complete the following table by adding the characteristics of the plantlike protists.*

Plantlike Protist Phylum	Characteristics
Dinoflagellates	4.
Chrysophytes	5.
Diatoms	6.

Reviewing Key Skills

7. **Applying Concepts** What are two important ecological roles of phytoplankton?

   _____

   _____

   _____

8. **Inferring** You notice an algal bloom in the water. What does this tell you about the condition of the water? How will the algal bloom affect organisms in the water?

   _____

   _____

   _____

Chapter 20 Protists

Reviewing Key Concepts

Identification *On the lines provided, identify which features describe the following types of algae:* red algae, brown algae, *and* green algae.

_____ 1. phycobilins increase their efficiency in harvesting sunlight, enabling them to live at great depths

_____ 2. largest, most complex of the algae; mostly marine; commonly found in shallow waters

_____ 3. share many characteristics with plants, including photosynthetic pigments and cell wall composition

Identifying Structures *On the lines provided, identify each structure formed during the life cycle of the green algae* Ulva *as being either* haploid *or* diploid.

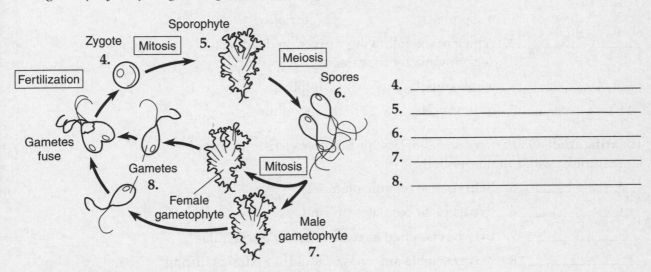

4. _____

5. _____

6. _____

7. _____

8. _____

Reviewing Key Skills

9. **Predicting** Listed below are certain environmental situations. For each situation, decide whether it would be more advantageous for algae to undergo sexual or asexual reproduction. Explain your answer.

   a. Green algae live in a pond that is beginning to freeze.

   _____

   _____

   b. A factory that manufactures fertilizer accidentally releases plant fertilizers into a nearby lake. There is now a great deal of nutrients for the green algae living in the lake.

   _____

   _____

Reviewing Key Concepts

Multiple Choice *On the lines provided, write the letter of the answer that best completes the sentence or answers the question.*

_____ **1.** Funguslike protists obtain nutrients through

    a. predation.   c. photosynthesis.

    b. respiration.   d. their cell membranes.

_____ **2.** What do funguslike protists have that fungi do not?

    a. cell walls   c. centrioles

    b. chlorophyll   d. chitin

_____ **3.** Which of the following is NOT found in funguslike protists?

    a. chitin cell wall   c. cell membrane

    b. spores   d. centrioles

_____ **4.** Which of the following thrives on dead or decaying matter in water?

    a. plasmodia   c. hyphae

    b. oomycetes   d. oogonium

Identification *On the lines provided, classify each characteristic as that of* slime molds, water molds, *or* both.

_____ **5.** help recycle organic material

_____ **6.** live as plant parasites on land

_____ **7.** may be classified as either cellular or acellular

_____ **8.** may resemble amoebas or moldlike clumps during different stages of life

Reviewing Key Skills

9. Comparing and Contrasting Explain the similarities and differences of the multicellular stages of acellular and cellular slime molds.

_____

_____

_____

_____

10. Applying Concepts How do funguslike protists benefit plants? How do they harm plants?

_____

_____

_____

_____

Name_____ Class_____ Date _____

Multiple Choice *On the lines provided, write the letter of the answer that best answers each question.*

_____ 1. What is the name of the type of organism that is not a plant, an animal, a fungus, or a prokaryote?
  a. protist   c. bacterium
  b. phycobilin   d. spore

_____ 2. Extensions of cytoplasm for movement and feeding are called
  a. cilia.   c. trichocysts.
  b. pseudopods.   d. pellicles.

_____ 3. Amoeboid movement is a method of locomotion used by which of the following protozoans?
  a. Zooflagellates   c. Ciliates
  b. Sarcodines   d. Sporozoans

_____ 4. All of the following play a role in the digestive process of a paramecium EXCEPT the
  a. vacuoles.   c. anal pore.
  b. gullet.   d. trichocysts.

_____ 5. What structures do paramecia use for protection?
  a. contractile vacuoles   c. filaments
  b. pellicles   d. trichocysts

_____ 6. Of the two nuclei found in a ciliate, which one contains a "reserve copy" of all the cell's genes?
  a. micronucleus   c. macronucleus
  b. nucleolus   d. nuclear membrane

_____ 7. What process allows paramecia to exchange genetic material with other paramecia?
  a. asexual reproduction   c. alternation of generations
  b. binary fission   d. conjugation

_____ 8. What is the function of structure A in the diagram of the paramecium shown below?
  a. temporarily stores food
  b. collects, then pumps water out of the organism
  c. releases spiny projections that protect the cell
  d. used for feeding and movement

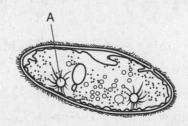

_____ 9. What compounds do many algae have to help them absorb light at different wavelengths?
  a. lipids
  b. proteins
  c. accessory pigments
  d. DNA and RNA

_____ 10. What structure in euglenophytes help them to detect light?
  a. a pellicle
  b. an eyespot
  c. a flagellum
  d. a micronucleus

_____ 11. What is the name of the membrane that covers a euglena?
  a. a trichocyst
  b. a pellicle
  c. a stipe
  d. a blade

_____ 12. What structures do sporophytes use in reproduction?
  a. trichocysts
  b. pellicles
  c. stipes
  d. spores

Completion *On the lines provided, complete the following sentences.*

13. The small, photosynthetic organisms found near the surface of the ocean are called _____.

14. The accessory pigments found in red algae that are especially good at absorbing blue light are called _____.

15. The freshwater alga *Spirogyra* forms long threadlike colonies called

_____.

16. The process in which many types of algae switch back and forth between haploid and diploid stages during their life cycles is called

_____.

17. The gamete-producing haploid form of the green alga *Ulva* is known as a(an) _____.

18. The diploid form of *Ulva* is known as a(an) _____ because it produces spores.

Matching *On the lines provided, write the letter of the word that best matches each description.*

  a. cellular slime mold
  b. acellular slime mold
  c. plasmodium
  d. hyphae
  e. zoosporangium
  f. antheridium
  g. oogonium

_____ 19. single structure of a slime mold with many nuclei

_____ 20. a spore case

_____ 21. has distinct cells during every phase of its life cycle

_____ 22. produces female nuclei in water molds

_____ 23. thin filaments produced by water molds

_____ 24. pass through a stage in which their cells fuse to form large cells with many nuclei

_____ 25. produces male nuclei in water molds

Toxic Algal Blooms

Algae, or phytoplankton, play a number of roles in the Earth's ecosystem. Most algae are harmless and serve as an important food source for a wide array of organisms. In addition, algae perform much of the photosynthesis that occurs on Earth and thus are an important source of oxygen. Of the thousands of species of algae, however, a few dozen produce dangerous toxins. Some of these toxins may harm humans who are directly exposed to them. Other toxins become a danger when they accumulate in the fish or shellfish that people eat.

The term *red tide* is commonly used to describe the blooms of these toxin-producing algae that form after a period of extremely rapid growth. During a bloom, the algal population in the water is so large and densely packed that reddish pigments in the algae cause the water to appear red.

The term red tide is somewhat misleading. Not all of the algae that possess the reddish pigments seen in a red tide actually produce toxins. In fact, there are algae that produce toxins, but don't possess reddish pigments. Further, those algae that possess both toxins and reddish pigments may be harmful in concentrations that are too low to actually cause the water to appear red. For these reasons, scientists now use the term "harmful algal bloom," or HAB.

The dinoflagellate *Alexandrium tamarense* produces toxins that lead to paralytic shellfish poisoning, or PSP. Filter feeders like mussels, clams, oysters, and scallops eat algae and tend to accumulate toxins. Typically, humans develop PSP after eating shellfish contaminated with toxins. PSP is potentially fatal and epidemics can occur without an observable red tide.

Because there is no antidote for PSP, the illness must be prevented. Careful and regular monitoring of toxin levels in the shellfish populations is essential. By law, the harvest of shellfish is generally restricted to specific areas that are then carefully and regularly monitored. When a harmful algal bloom occurs, even if there is no red tide, monitoring will detect dangerous levels of toxins that appear in the shellfish. As a precaution, fishing and harvest from the area in which contaminated shellfish were found is prohibited. This helps to ensure that people are served only seafood that is free of dangerous toxins.

Evaluation *On the lines provided, answer the following questions.*

1. What is the risk of poaching shellfish from an area that is not open to harvest?

_____

_____

_____

2. Why might the blooming behavior of an algae population make it a better food source for other marine animals?

_____

_____

_____

Chapter 20 Protists   **Graphic Organizer**

Concept Map

Using information from the chapter, complete the concept map below. If there is not enough room in the concept map to write your answers, write them on a separate sheet of paper.

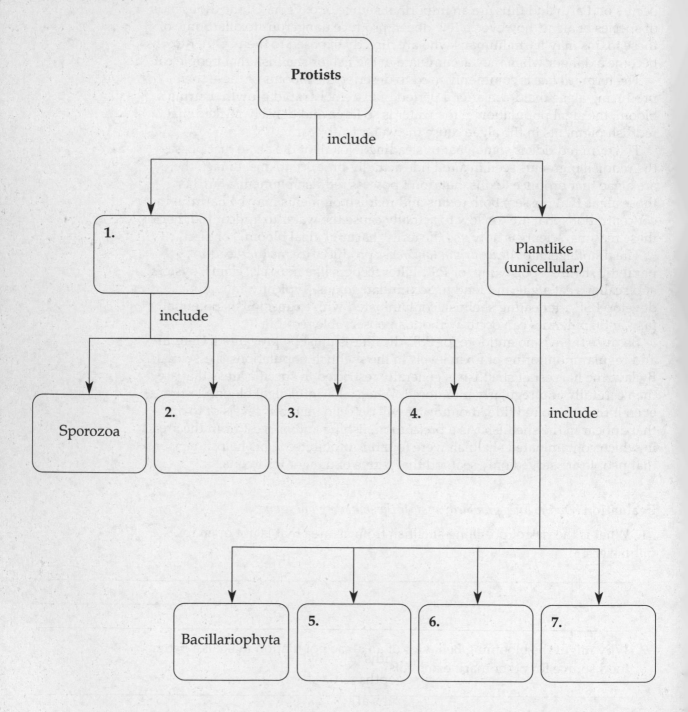

Multiple Choice

Write the letter that best answers the question or completes the statement on the line provided.

_____ 1. Multicellular protists are grouped with unicellular protists because multicellular protists
   a. do not resemble plants.
   b. do not resemble animals.
   c. do not resemble fungi.
   d. are so similar to unicellular protists.

_____ 2. According to biologist Lynn Margulis, eukaryotic cells may have evolved from
   a. a symbiosis of several cells.
   b. mitochondria that grew very large.
   c. chloroplasts that grew very large.
   d. plants, animals, and fungi.

_____ 3. Many zooflagellates live in lakes and streams, where they obtain food by
   a. penetrating and living within cells of a host.
   b. absorbing food through their cell membranes.
   c. sweeping food particles into their gullet.
   d. surrounding their meal and taking it inside themselves.

_____ 4. Which of the following diseases does the animallike protist known as *Entamoeba* cause?
   a. malaria
   b. African sleeping sickness
   c. amebic dysentery
   d. potato blight

_____ 5. As sunlight passes through sea water, the sea water
   a. absorbs large amounts of red and violet wavelengths.
   b. reflects large amounts of red and violet wavelengths.
   c. absorbs large amounts of blue wavelengths.
   d. none of the above

_____ 6. What effect did the evolution of different forms of chlorophyll have in algae?
   a. a decrease in the range of depths at which algae can live
   b. an increase in the range of depths at which algae can live
   c. no effect on the range of depths at which algae can live
   d. a reduction in the photosynthetic capacity of algae

_____ 7. Which of the statements is true about dinoflagellates?

    a. They contain bright yellow pigments.

    b. They can be both photosynthetic and heterotrophic.

    c. Many species are luminescent.

    d. They possess pillbox-shaped cell walls of silica.

_____ 8. The population of small, photosynthetic organisms found near the surface of the ocean are called

    a. chrysophytes.   c. phytoplankton.

    b. pyrophytes.   d. diatoms.

_____ 9. What characteristic of green plants is shared by green algae?

    a. cell wall composition

    b. photosynthetic pigments

    c. multicellularity

    d. all of the above

_____10. Red algae lack flagella and

    a. nuclei.   c. accessory pigments.

    b. centrioles.   d. chlorophyll.

_____11. In the life cycle of the green alga *Ulva*, the phase that produces male and female gametes is known as a

    a. sporophyte.

    b. gametophyte.

    c. spore.

    d. zoospore.

_____12. Some products derived from algae include

    a. drugs for stomach ulcers and high blood pressure.

    b. thickeners for food.

    c. chemicals in plastics, waxes, paints, and lubricants.

    d. all of the above

_____13. Funguslike protists get nutrients by

    a. photosynthesis.

    b. living as an animal parasite.

    c. absorbing them from dead or decaying matter.

    d. none of the above

_____14. In oomycetes, sexual reproduction takes place in the

    a. migrating colony.   c. antheridium and oogonium.

    b. sporangium.   d. zoosporangium.

_____15. The work of funguslike protists and other decomposers is important in improving the quality of

    a. salt water.   c. topsoil.

    b. fresh water.   d. potato crops.

Completion

Complete each statement on the line provided.

16. Animallike protists that use structures called _____ for movement and for feeding are members of the phylum Sarcodina.

17. Many members of the phylum Pyrrophyta, which are also referred to as _____ , are luminescent.

18. Red algae contain reddish accessory pigments as well as _____ , one of the three types of chlorophyll.

19. Because algae carry out _____ , they produce much of Earth's atmospheric oxygen.

20. The funguslike protists that cause several serious plant diseases, including mildews and blights of grapes and tomatoes, are the _____ .

Short Answer

In complete sentences, write the answers to the questions on the lines provided.

21. How do sporozoans differ from other animallike protists in terms of movement?

   _____

   _____

22. What is the function of chlorophyll and accessory pigments in algae?

   _____

   _____

23. What are "red tides," and why are they dangerous?

   _____

   _____

   _____

24. Compare the structure and function of the diploid sporophyte to the haploid gametophyte in the multicellular alga *Ulva*.

   _____

   _____

   _____

25. What is the primary difference between cellular slime molds and acellular slime molds?

   _____

   _____

   _____

Name_____ Class_____ Date _____

Using Science Skills

Use the diagram below to answer the following questions on the lines provided.

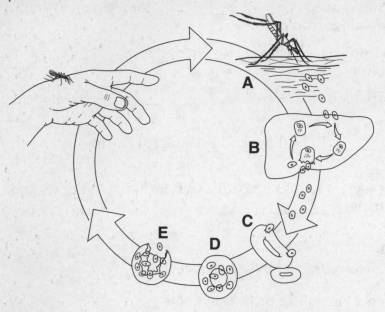

Figure 1

26. **Interpreting Graphics** What is the serious human disease whose pathway of infection is illustrated in Figure 1, and what organism causes the disease?

_____

27. **Inferring** Considering the nature of the animal that carries the protist shown in Figure 1, in what kinds of environments would this disease be most common?

_____

_____

_____

_____

28. **Interpreting Graphics** According to Figure 1, what has occurred up to and including Step B?

_____

_____

_____

_____

29. **Interpreting Graphics** According to Figure 1, what is occurring in Steps C, D, and E?

_____

_____

_____

30. Predicting Infection by the protist shown in Figure 1 produces periods of acute illness followed by periods of reduced symptoms. These periods follow each other in repeating cycles. Predict which part of the cycle of infection results in acute illness and an increase in symptoms.

_____

_____

_____

_____

Essay

Write the answer to each question in the space provided.

31. Identify the cause and symptoms of African sleeping sickness, and explain how it is spread.

32. Describe the appearance of a typical euglena, and explain how it moves through water.

33. Compare the structure of the colonial alga, *Volvox*, with that of *Ulva*, a true multicellular alga.

34. Why is it difficult to classify cellular slime molds as unicellular or multicellular?

35. What might be the end result in terrestrial and aquatic ecosystems if all decomposers—including slime molds and water molds—no longer existed?

Chapter 20 Protists   **Chapter Test B**

Multiple Choice

Write the letter that best answers the question or completes the statement on the line provided.

_____ 1. A protist is any organism that is not a plant, an animal, a fungus, or a(an)
   a. eukaryote.
   b. prokaryote.
   c. eubacterium.

_____ 2. In an amoeba, a small cavity within the cytoplasm that stores food is called a
   a. gullet.
   b. pseudopod.
   c. food vacuole.

_____ 3. To which phylum do amoebas, foraminifers, and heliozoans belong?
   a. sarcodines
   b. ciliates
   c. sporozoans

_____ 4. The zooflagellate *Trypanosoma* causes the disease known as
   a. malaria.
   b. African sleeping sickness.
   c. amebic dysentery.

_____ 5. Which substances allow algae to harvest and use the energy from sunlight?
   a. cilium and fucoxanthin
   b. chlorophyll and accessory pigments
   c. phycobilin and flagellum

_____ 6. Euglenas have an intricate, folded cell membrane called a(an)
   a. cell wall.
   b. trichocyst.
   c. pellicle.

_____ 7. An algal bloom is
   a. the clouding of water by sewage.
   b. an enormous mass of algae.
   c. a symbiotic relationship between algae and coral.

_____ 8. An example of a multicellular green alga is
   a. *Ulva.*
   b. *Chlamydomonas.*
   c. *Volvox.*

____ 9. The switching back and forth between a diploid and haploid stage in a life cycle is called
    a. alternation of generations.
    b. fusion of opposite mating types.
    c. sexual reproduction.

____10. The green alga *Chlamydomonas* reproduces asexually by producing
    a. gametophytes.
    b. sporophytes.
    c. zygotes.

____11. What very large type of algae lives off the coasts of North America?
    a. rockweed
    b. sea lettuce
    c. giant kelp

____12. Which of the following groups includes only funguslike protists?
    a. cellular slime molds, brown algae, water molds
    b. cellular slime molds, acellular slime molds, water molds
    c. cellular slime molds, acellular slime molds, animallike protists

____13. The funguslike protists that thrive on dead or decaying organic matter in water are
    a. water molds.
    b. acellular slime molds.
    c. cellular slime molds.

____14. When the amoebalike cells of acellular slime molds fuse, they form structures with many nuclei called
    a. plasmodia.
    b. zoosporangia.
    c. spores.

____15. Organisms that break down organic material include the
    a. funguslike protists.
    b. animallike protists.
    c. plantlike protists.

Completion

Complete each statement on the line provided.

16. Eukaryotes that are not members of the kingdoms Plantae, Animalia, or Fungi are _____ .

17. The sporozoan *Plasmodium*, carried from host to host by mosquitoes, causes _____ , a very serious infectious disease.

18. In the human body, *Plasmodium* first infects liver cells and then _____ cells, causing them to burst.

19. Chlorophyll and accessory pigments allow algae to harvest and use the energy of _____ .

20. Funguslike protists are _____ that absorb nutrients from dead or decaying organic matter.

Short Answer

In complete sentences, write the answers to the questions on the lines provided.

21. Explain the importance of the animallike protist *Trichonympha* to the termites in which it grows.

_____

_____

_____

22. What is phytoplankton?

_____

_____

_____

_____

_____

23. What are two human uses of algae?

_____

_____

_____

_____

_____

24. What are slime molds?

_____

_____

_____

_____

_____

25. What caused the destruction of much of the potato crops of 1845 and 1846 in Ireland?

_____

_____

_____

_____

_____

Using Science Skills

Use the diagram below to answer the following questions on the lines provided.

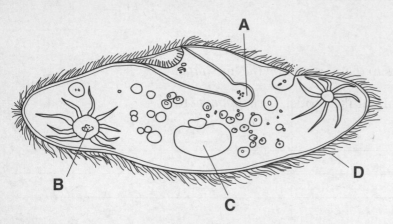

Figure 1

26. **Interpreting Graphics** Figure 1 shows a diagram of an organism. Is it a single-celled or a multicellular organism?

_____

_____

27. **Inferring** Structure A opens to the outside of the organism shown in Figure 1. How is the structure of A related to its function in the organism?

_____

_____

_____

28. **Predicting** If the structure labeled B in Figure 1 was to malfunction, what effect would this likely have on the organism?

_____

_____

29. **Inferring** How does the structure labeled C in Figure 1 help the organism in its day-to-day existence?

_____

_____

_____

30. **Predicting** If the structure labeled D in Figure 1 were to malfunction, what effect would this likely have on the organism?

_____

_____

LESSON PLAN 21–1 (pages 527–529)

The Kingdom Fungi

Time
1 period
1/2 block

Section Objectives

- **21.1.1 Identify** the defining characteristics of fungi.
- **21.1.2 Describe** the main structures of a fungus.
- **21.1.3 Explain** how fungi reproduce.

Vocabulary chitin • hypha • mycelium • fruiting body • sporangium • sporangiophore

Local Standards

1 FOCUS

Reading Strategy
Students copy the Key Concepts into their notebooks and then write supporting details as they read the section.

Targeted Resources
- ❏ Transparencies: **316** Section 21–1 Interest Grabber
- ❏ Transparencies: **317** Section 21–1 Outline

2 INSTRUCT

Build Science Skills: Comparing and Contrasting
Students make a table to compare and contrast bacteria, protists, fungi, plants, and animals. **L2**

Use Visuals: Figure 21–2
Use Figure 21–2 to review fungus structure and function. **L1 L2**

Build Science Skills: Designing Experiments
Students design experiments that test what conditions would cause a fungus to reproduce sexually. **L3**

Build Science Skills: Observing
Students observe mushroom spores under a microscope. **L2**

Targeted Resources
- ❏ Reading and Study Workbook: Section 21–1
- ❏ Adapted Reading and Study Workbook: Section 21–1
- ❏ Teaching Resources: Section Summaries 21–1, Worksheets 21–1
- ❏ Transparencies: **318** Hyphae Structure, **319** Figure 21–2 The Structure of a Mushroom

3 ASSESS

Evaluate Understanding
Have students explain the different parts of Figure 21–2.

Reteach
Students draw and label a typical fungus, as in Figure 21–2.

Targeted Resources
- ❏ Teaching Resources: Section Review 21–1
- ❏ ⓘ**Text** Section 21–1

LESSON PLAN 21–2 (pages 530–536)

Time
2 periods
1 block

Classification of Fungi

Section Objective

Local Standards

■ **21.2.1 Identify** the characteristics of the four main groups of fungi.

Vocabulary zygospore • rhizoid • stolon • gametangium • conidium • ascus • ascospore • budding • basidium • basidiospore

1 FOCUS

Reading Strategy
Students record the names of the main groups of fungi on notecards and then add characteristics of each group as they read.

Targeted Resources
❑ Transparencies: **320** Section 21–2 Interest Grabber, **321** Section 21–2 Outline, **322** Concept Map

2 INSTRUCT

Quick Lab
Students observe the major structures of a mold and hypothesize why bread mold produces many sporangia. **L2** **L3**

Use Visuals: Figure 21–6
Use Figure 21–6 to review the life cycle of ascomycetes. **L2**

Use Visuals: Figure 21–8
Use Figure 21–8 to review the life cycle of basidiomycetes. **L1** **L2**

Build Science Skills: Using Models
Students make models of basidiomycetes, using modeling compound. **L2**

Use Visuals: Figure 21–10
Use Figure 21–10 to review use of the deuteromycete *Penicillium*. **L1** **L2**

Targeted Resources
❑ Reading and Study Workbook: Section 21–2

❑ Adapted Reading and Study Workbook: Section 21–2

❑ Transparencies: **323** Figure 21–5 The Life Cycle of *Rhizopus*, **324** Figure 21–7 The Life Cycle of an Ascomycete, **325** Figure 21–8 The Life Cycle of a Basidiomycete

❑ Teaching Resources: Section Summaries 21–2, Worksheets 21–2, Enrichment

❑ Lab Manual A: Chapter 21 Lab

❑ Lab Manual B: Chapter 21 Lab

❑ **NSTA** *sci*$_{LINKS}$ Fungi

❑ **NSTA** *sci*$_{LINKS}$ Asexual reproduction

3 ASSESS

Evaluate Understanding
Students compare and contrast the life cycles of a sac fungus and a club fungus.

Reteach
Students make a compare-and-contrast table to organize information about the four main groups of fungi.

Targeted Resources
❑ Teaching Resources: Section Review 21–2

❑ **iText** Section 21–2

LESSON PLAN 21–3 (pages 537–542)

Ecology of Fungi

Section Objectives

- **21.3.1 Explain** what the ecological role of fungi is.
- **21.3.2 Describe** problems that parasitic fungi cause.
- **21.3.3 Describe** the kinds of mutualistic relationships that fungi form with other organisms.

Vocabulary saprobe • lichen • mycorrhiza

Local Standards

1 FOCUS

Vocabulary Preview
Have students divide each of the Vocabulary words into syllables.

Targeted Resources
❏ Transparencies: **326** Section 21–3 Interest Grabber
❏ Transparencies: **327** Section 21–3 Outline

2 INSTRUCT

Make Connections: Earth Science
To reinforce the concept of fungi as decomposers, focus students' attention on the humus in potting soil. **L1** **L2**

Make Connections: Health Science
Students focus on the kind of environment in which fungal parasites spread. **L1** **L2**

Use Visuals: Figure 21–16
Use Figure 21–16 to reinforce an understanding of the structure of lichens. **L1** **L2**

Build Science Skills: Observing
Students observe photos and find examples of different species of lichens. **L1** **L2**

Problem Solving
Students consider a problem related to the importance of mycorrhizae for plants. **L2** **L3**

Targeted Resources
❏ Reading and Study Workbook: Section 21–3
❏ Adapted Reading and Study Workbook: Section 21–3
❏ Teaching Resources: Section Summaries 21–3, Worksheets 21–3
❏ Transparencies: **328** Lichen Structure
❏ Lab Worksheets: Chapter 21 Real-World Lab

3 ASSESS

Evaluate Understanding
Have students compare different symbiotic relationships involving fungi.

Reteach
Students make a chart listing beneficial and harmful roles fungi play in the environment.

Targeted Resources
❏ Teaching Resources: Section Review 21–3, Chapter Vocabulary Review, Graphic Organizer, Chapter 21 Tests: Levels A and B
❏ Lab Assessment: Laboratory Assessment 3
❏ *i* Text Section 21–3, Chapter 21 Assessment
❏ **PHSchool.com** Online Chapter 21 Test

Chapter 21   Fungi

Summary

21–1 The Kingdom Fungi

Fungi are eukaryotic heterotrophs with cell walls made of chitin. Chitin is a complex carbohydrate. Fungi do not ingest their food. Instead, fungi digest food outside their bodies and then absorb it.

All fungi except for yeasts are multicellular. Multicellular fungi are made up of thin filaments called **hyphae** (singular: hypha). Each hypha is only one cell thick. **The bodies of multicellular fungi are made of hyphae tangled together into a thick mass called a mycelium.** The **mycelium** allows a large surface area to come into contact with the food source through which the fungi grow. The **fruiting body** of a fungus is a reproductive structure growing from the mycelium in the soil beneath it. In a mushroom, the fruiting body is the aboveground part of the mushroom.

Most fungi reproduce both asexually and sexually.

- Asexual reproduction can occur when cells or hyphae break off and begin to grow on their own. Some fungi also make spores. In some fungi, spores are formed in structures called **sporangia.** Sporangia are found at the tips of hyphae called **sporangiophores.**

- Sexual reproduction in fungi usually involves two different mating types. One type is called "+" (plus), and the other is called "−" (minus). When the hyphae of a "+" fungus meets the hyphae of a "−" fungus, they fuse together in the same cell. After a period of growth and development, the nuclei form a diploid zygote. The diploid zygote enters meiosis, and produces haploid spores.

Spores of fungi exist in almost every environment. Many fungi produce dry, almost weightless spores that are easily scattered by wind. For these spores to grow, they must land in a favorable environment. Temperature, moisture, and food conditions must be in the right combination. Most spores, therefore, do not grow into mature organisms.

21–2 Classification of Fungi

There are four main groups of fungi: common molds, sac fungi, club fungi, and imperfect fungi. Fungi are classified according to their methods of reproduction and their structure.

Common molds (phylum Zygomycota) grow on meat, cheese, and bread. **These fungi have a life cycle that includes a zygospore.** A **zygospore** is a resting spore that contains zygotes formed during the sexual phase of the mold's life cycle.

Common molds include the black bread mold. During the sexual phase in black bread mold, hyphae from different mating types fuse to form gamete-making structures called **gametangia.** Black bread mold has two kinds of hyphae.

- The rootlike hyphae that go through the bread's surface are rhizoids.
- The stemlike hyphae that run along the surface of bread are stolons.

Sac fungi (phylum Ascomycota) include the large cup fungi and the unicellular yeasts. **These fungi are named for the ascus, a reproductive structure that contains spores.** The life cycle of an ascomycete includes both sexual and asexual reproduction.

In sexual reproduction, haploid hyphae from two different mating types (+ and −) grow close together to make a fruiting body. An **ascus** forms within the fruiting body. Two nuclei of different mating types fuse within the ascus to form a diploid zygote. Asexual reproduction in cup fungi and yeast are different.

- In cup fungi, tiny spores called **conidia** form at the tips of specialized hyphae called conidiophores.
- Asexual reproduction in yeast occurs by cell division. This process is called **budding.**

Club fungi (phylum Basidiomycota) include mushrooms, shelf fungi, and puffballs. **These fungi have a reproductive structure that resembles a club.** The cap of the fruiting body of a basidiomycete is made up of tightly packed hyphae. The lower side of the cap has gills, thin blades of tissue lined with basidia. A **basidium** is a spore-bearing structure. Two nuclei in each basidium fuse to form a diploid zygote cell. The zygote cell undergoes meiosis, forming clusters of spores called **basidiospores.** A single mushroom can produce billions of basidiospores.

Imperfect fungi **(phylum Deuteromycota) include fungi that are not placed in other phyla because researchers have never been able to observe a sexual phase in their life cycles.** An example of an imperfect fungus is *Penicillium notatum*, a mold that grows on fruit. It is the source of the antibiotic penicillin.

21–3 Ecology of Fungi

All fungi are heterotrophs. Some fungi are saprobes. **Saprobes are organisms that obtain food from decaying organic matter. Fungi play an essential role in maintaining balance in ecosystems. Fungi recycle nutrients as they break down the remains and wastes of other organisms.** Many fungi feed by releasing digestive enzymes that break down organic material into simple molecules. In breaking down this matter, fungi help recycle nutrients and essential chemicals. Without such decomposers, the energy-rich compounds that organisms accumulate would be lost forever.

Parasitic fungi cause plant and animal diseases. A few cause diseases in humans.

- Fungal diseases in plants include corn smut and wheat rust.
- Fungal diseases in humans include athlete's foot, ringworm, thrush, and yeast infections of the female reproductive tract.

Some fungi are symbiotes that form mutualistic relationships in which both partners benefit.

- **Lichens** are an association between a fungus and green alga, a cyanobacterium, or both. The alga or cyanobacterium provides the fungus with a source of energy by carrying out photosynthesis. The fungus provides the photosynthetic organism with water and minerals and shades it from intense sunlight.
- Mutualistic associations of plant roots and fungi are called **mycorrhizae.** The hyphae of fungi aid the plant in absorbing water and minerals. The fungi also release enzymes that free nutrients from the soil. The plant provides the fungi with the products of photosynthesis. The presence of mycorrhizae is needed for the growth of many plants.

Hyphae Structure

Hyphae are thin filaments that make up multicellular fungi. Each hypha is one cell thick. Some hyphae have cross walls that divide each hypha into cells with one or two nuclei. Other hyphae lack cross walls and have many nuclei.

In each diagram, label the following structures: cell wall, cytoplasm, cross wall, nuclei. *Some structures appear in both diagrams.*

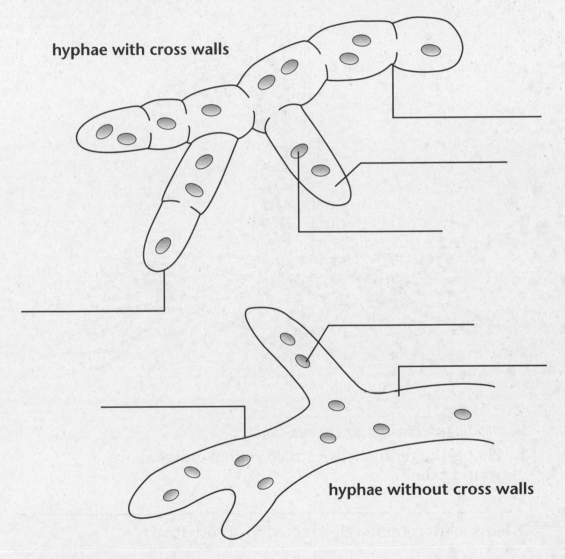

hyphae with cross walls

hyphae without cross walls

Circle the correct answer.

1. What makes up the cell walls of hyphae?

   chitin   mycelium

2. What is the thick mass of tangled hyphae that makes up most fungi called?

   mycelium   yeast

Fungus Structure

A multicellular fungus is made up of many hyphae tangled together in a thick mass. This mass of hyphae is called the mycelium. The mycelium produces a reproductive structure called a fruiting body. One mycelium can produce many fruiting bodies.

Color the hyphae *red. Then label the* fruiting body *and the* mycelium.

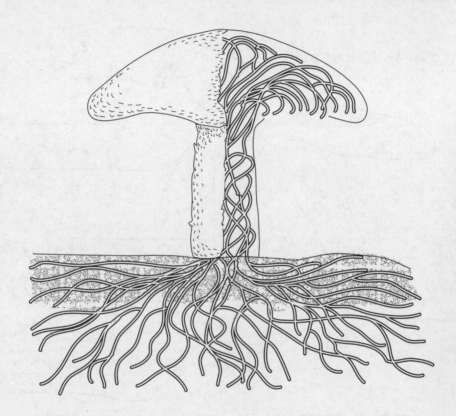

Use the diagram to answer the questions.

1. What is the reproductive structure that grows above ground called?

_____

2. How is mycelium well-adapted to absorb food?

_____

_____

Bread Mold Life Cycle

A bread mold can reproduce both sexually and asexually. In asexual reproduction, the mold directly produces spores. In sexual reproduction, a zygospore forms that contains zygotes. These zygotes can undergo meiosis and form spores.

Color the arrow that shows asexual reproduction red. Color the arrows that show sexual reproduction blue.

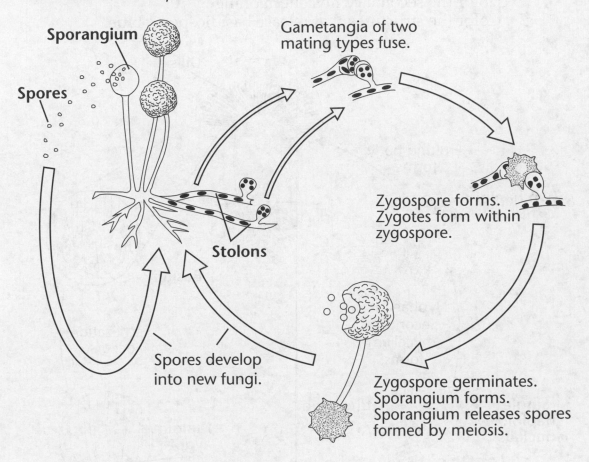

Use the diagram to answer the questions.

1. Which structure releases spores? Circle the correct answer.

    sporangium   gametangia

2. The zygospore can remain dormant for long periods before it germinates. Why might this be useful to a fungus?

_____

_____

_____

Club Fungi Life Cycle

Club fungi, or basidiomycetes, reproduce sexually through the fusion of nuclei found in structures called basidia.

Follow the prompts below to identify important stages in the life cycle of club fungi.

- Color the fruiting body red.
- Color the primary mycelium yellow.
- Color the secondary mycelium orange.
- Color the structures that release basidiospores blue.

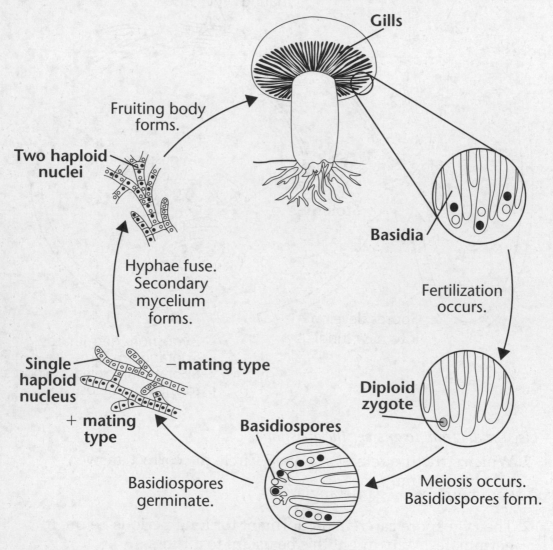

Use the diagram to answer the questions.

1. What do basidiospores grow into?

_____

2. What are the spore-bearing structures called? Circle the correct

answer.   basidia   primary mycelium

Lichens

Lichens are formed by the symbiotic relationship of a fungus and a photosynthetic organism. The lichen shown below is composed of fungi and algae. It grows on rock.

Color the hyphae of the fungus brown. Color the algae green. Then label the algae *and* hyphae.

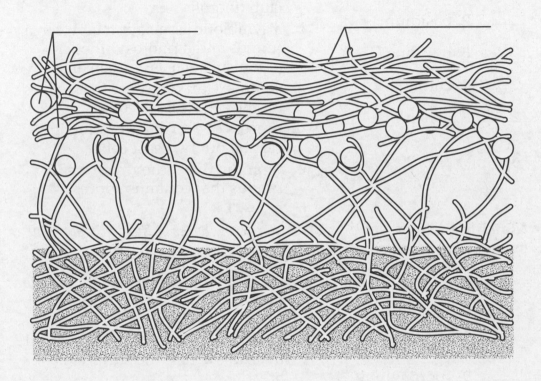

Answer the questions.

1. Which term best describes the relationship between the algae and the fungus in the diagram above? Circle the correct answer.

   parasitic   mutualistic

2. What do the algae provide for the fungus?

   _____

3. What does the fungus provide for the algae?

   _____

Chapter 21   Fungi

Vocabulary Review

Matching   *In the space provided, write the letter of the definition that best matches each term.*

_____ **1.** ascus

_____ **2.** basidium

_____ **3.** budding

_____ **4.** chitin

_____ **5.** lichen

a. the spore-bearing structure of a club fungus

b. a symbiotic association between a fungus and a photosynthetic organism such as a green alga

c. complex carbohydrate that makes up the cell walls of fungi

d. process of asexual reproduction carried out by yeast cells

e. reproductive structure of a sac fungus that contains spores

Matching   *In the space provided, write the letter of the definition that best matches each term.*

_____ **6.** mycelium

_____ **7.** rhizoid

_____ **8.** saprobe

_____ **9.** sporangium

_____ **10.** stolon

a. mass of tangled hyphae that makes up the body of a multicellular fungus

b. a stemlike hypha on a bread mold that runs across the surface of bread

c. a structure that contains spores in a bread mold

d. an organism that obtains food from decaying organic matter

e. a rootlike hypha that anchors a bread mold to the bread

Summary

21–1 The Kingdom Fungi

Fungi are eukaryotic heterotrophs that have cell walls. The cell walls of fungi are made up of chitin, a complex carbohydrate. Fungi do not ingest their food, as animals do. Instead, fungi digest food outside their bodies and then absorb it. Many fungi feed by absorbing nutrients from decaying matter. Some fungi are parasites.

All fungi except for yeasts are multicellular. Multicellular fungi are composed of thin filaments called hyphae. Each hypha is only one cell thick. The bodies of multicellular fungi are composed of many hyphae tangled together into a thick mass called a mycelium. The fruiting body of a fungus—such as the above-ground part of a mushroom—is a reproductive structure growing from the mycelium in the soil beneath it.

Most fungi reproduce both asexually and sexually. Asexual reproduction can occur when cells or hyphae break off and begin to grow on their own. Some fungi also produce spores. In some fungi, spores are produced in structures called sporangia. Sporangia are found at the tips of hyphae called sporangiophores. Sexual reproduction in fungi usually involves two different mating types.

Spores of fungi are found in almost every environment. Many fungi produce dry, almost weightless spores that are easily scattered in the wind.

21–2 Classification of Fungi

Fungi are classified according to their structure and method of reproduction. The four main groups of fungi are the common molds (phylum Zygomycota), the sac fungi (phylum Ascomycota), the club fungi (phylum Basidiomycota), and the imperfect fungi (Deuteromycota).

The common molds—zygomycetes—grow on meat, cheese, and bread. Zygomycetes have a life cycle that includes a zygospore. A zygospore is a resting spore that contains zygotes formed during the sexual phase of the mold's life cycle. The zygomycetes include the black bread mold, *Rhizopus stolonifer*. Black bread mold has two different kinds of hyphae. The rootlike hyphae that penetrate the bread's surface are rhizoids. The stemlike hyphae that run along the surface of bread are stolons. During the sexual phase in the bread mold, hyphae from different mating types fuse to produce gamete-forming structures called gametangia.

Sac fungi—ascomycetes—have a reproductive structure called an ascus, which contains spores. Sac fungi include the large cup fungi as well as the unicellular yeasts. The life cycle of an ascomycete includes both asexual and sexual reproduction. In asexual reproduction, tiny spores called conidia form at the tips of specialized hyphae called conidiophores. In sexual reproduction, haploid hyphae from two different mating types (+ and –) grow close together and produce a fruiting body. An ascus forms within the fruiting body. Two nuclei of different mating types fuse within the ascus to form a diploid zygote. Yeasts are unicellular ascomycetes. The process of asexual reproduction in yeasts is called budding.

The club fungi—basidiomycetes—have a specialized reproductive structure that resembles a club. The cap of the fruiting body of a basidiomycete—such as the familiar mushroom—is composed of tightly packed hyphae. The lower side of the cap is composed of gills, which are thin blades of tissue lined with basidia. A basidium is a spore-bearing structure. Two nuclei in each basidium fuse to form a diploid zygote cell. The zygote cell undergoes meiosis, forming clusters of spores called basidiospores. A single mushroom can produce billions of basidiospores. Club fungi include mushrooms, shelf fungi, and puffballs.

The imperfect fungi—deuteromycetes—include those fungi that are not placed in other phyla because researchers have never been able to observe a sexual phase in their life cycles. Most imperfect fungi look like ascomycetes, though others are similar to basidiomycetes or zygomycetes. An example of an imperfect fungus is *Penicillium notatum*, a mold that grows on fruit. It is the source of the antibiotic penicillin.

21–3 Ecology of Fungi

All fungi are heterotrophs. Many fungi are saprobes, which are organisms that obtain food from decaying organic matter. Others are parasites, and still others live in symbiosis with other species.

Fungi play an essential role in maintaining equilibrium in nearly every ecosystem. Fungi do this by recycling nutrients as they break down the bodies and wastes of other organisms. Many fungi feed by releasing digestive enzymes that break down organic material into simple molecules. Fungi food includes wastes and dead organisms. In breaking down this material, fungi promote the recycling of nutrients and essential chemicals. Without such decomposers, the energy-rich compounds that organisms accumulate would be lost forever.

Parasitic fungi cause serious plant and animal diseases. A few cause diseases in humans. Fungal diseases in plants include corn smut and wheat rust. Fungal diseases in humans include athlete's foot and ringworm, thrush, and yeast infections of the female reproductive tract.

Some fungi form symbiotic relationships in which both partners benefit, such as lichens and mycorrhizae. Lichens are not single organisms. Rather, lichens are symbiotic associations between a fungus and a photosynthetic organism. The photosynthetic organism in a lichen is either a green alga or a cyanobacterium, or both. The alga or cyanobacterium provides the fungus with a source of energy by carrying out photosynthesis. The fungus, in turn, provides the photosynthetic organism with water and minerals. The fungus also shades the alga or cyanobacterium from intense sunlight.

Mutualistic associations of plant roots and fungi are called mycorrhizae. The plant's roots are woven into a partnership with the web of fungal hyphae. The hyphae of fungi aid plants in absorbing water and minerals. In addition, the fungi release enzymes that free nutrients from the soil. The plants, in turn, provide the fungi with the products of photosynthesis. The presence of mycorrhizae is essential for the growth of many plants. Mycorrhizal associations were an adaptation that was critical in the evolution of plants.

Name_____ Class_____ Date _____

Section 21–1 The Kingdom Fungi (pages 527–529)

Key Concepts
- What are the defining characteristics of fungi?
- What is the internal structure of a fungus?
- How do fungi reproduce?

What Are Fungi? (page 527)

1. Circle the letter of each sentence that is true about fungi.

   a. They are heterotrophs.

   b. They have cell walls.

   c. They are photosynthetic.

   d. They are eukaryotic.

2. The cell walls of fungi are made of a complex carbohydrate called _____.

3. How do fungi digest their food? _____

   _____

4. Is the following sentence true or false? Some fungi are parasites. _____

Structure and Function of Fungi (pages 527–528)

5. Which group of fungi are not multicellular? _____

6. What are hyphae? _____

   _____

7. How thick is each hypha? _____

8. In some fungi, what divides the hyphae into cells containing one or two nuclei?

   _____

9. What is a mycelium? _____

   _____

   _____

10. Why is a mycelium well suited to absorb food? _____

    _____

    _____

11. What is a fruiting body of a fungus? _____

    _____

    _____

    _____

12. What is a fairy ring, and why does it form? _____
_____
_____

13. Label the parts of the fungus.

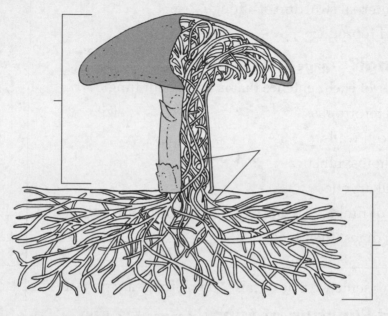

Reproduction in Fungi (pages 528–529)

14. Is the following sentence true or false? Most fungi can reproduce only asexually.

_____

15. How does asexual reproduction occur in fungi? _____
_____

_____

16. In some fungi, spores are produced in structures called _____.

17. Where are sporangia found in a fungus? _____
_____

_____

18. Sexual reproduction in fungi usually involves two different _____.

19. What is a gametangium? _____
_____

_____

_____

20. How does a zygote form in fungal sexual reproduction? _____

_____

_____

_____

_____

21. Circle the letter of each sentence that is true about sexual reproduction in fungi.

 a. The zygote is often the only diploid cell in the fungus's entire life cycle.

 b. Mating types are called male and female.

 c. Gametes of both mating types are about the same size.

 d. One mating type is a "+" (plus) and the other is a "−" (minus).

How Fungi Spread (page 529)

22. Is the following sentence true or false? The spores of many fungi scatter easily in the wind. _____

23. For a fungal spore to grow, where must it land? _____

_____

_____

_____

Section 21–2 Classification of Fungi (pages 530–536)

Key Concept
- What are the characteristics of the four main phyla of fungi?

Introduction (page 530)

1. Complete the concept map about the four main groups of fungi.

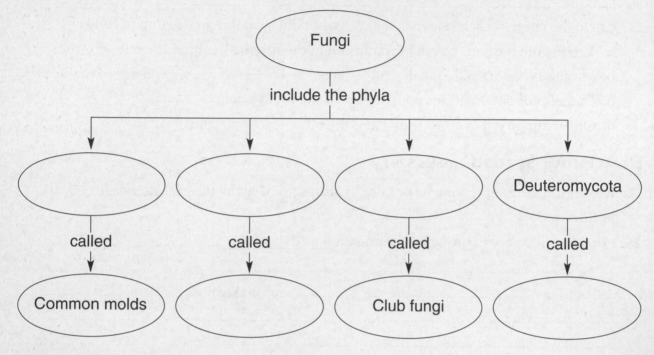

The Common Molds (pages 530–531)

2. What are zygomycetes? _____

_____

_____

3. The resting spore formed during the sexual phase of the mold's life cycle is called a(an)

_____.

4. Is the following sentence true or false? The hyphae of zygomycetes are generally

divided by cross walls. _____

5. What is the common name for *Rhizopus stolonifer*? _____

6. Complete the table about the kinds of hyphae of black bread mold.

KINDS OF HYPHAE

Kind	Description
Rhizoids	
Stolons	
	Hyphae that push up into the air and form sporangia at their tips

7. Complete the flowchart about sexual reproduction in zygomycetes.

> Two hyphae from different mating types come together, forming _____.

↓

> Haploid gametes from the mating types fuse to form diploid zygotes, which make up a single _____.

↓

> The zygospore eventually germinates, and a(an) _____ emerges.

↓

> The sporangium reproduces asexually by releasing _____.

The Sac Fungi (pages 532–533)

8. What is an ascus? _____
_____

9. Is the following sentence true or false? Ascomycetes make up the largest phylum in the kingdom Fungi. _____

10. What occurs among sac fungi during asexual reproduction? _____
_____
_____

11. Complete the flowchart about sexual reproduction in ascomycetes.

> Gametangia from two different mating types _____ together.

↓

> That fusion produces hyphae that contain haploid _____.

↓

> The N + N hyphae produce a fruiting body, inside of which the _____ forms.

↓

> Within the ascus, meiosis and mitosis occur to produce cells known as _____.

↓

> In a favorable environment, an ascospore germinates and grows into a haploid _____.

12. Is the following sentence true or false? Yeasts are multicellular ascomycetes.

_____

13. Why are yeasts classified as ascomycetes? _____

_____

14. What process do yeasts carry out to obtain energy when they are in a nutrient mixture such as bread dough? _____

The Club Fungi (pages 534–536)

15. From what does the phylum Basidiomycota get its name? _____

_____

16. Label the parts of a mushroom.

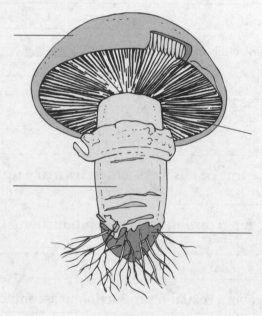

17. Where are basidia found on a basidiomycete? _____

_____

_____

18. The cap of a basidiomycete is composed of tightly packed _____.

19. Is the following sentence true or false? The remarkable growth of mushrooms overnight is caused by cell enlargement. _____

20. Circle the letter of each example of basidiomycetes.

    a. puffballs   **b.** shelf fungi   **c.** rusts   **d.** yeasts

21. Why should you never pick or eat any mushrooms found in the wild?

_____

_____

22. Complete the flowchart about reproduction in basidiomycetes.

```
┌────────────────────────────────────────────────────────────────────┐
│ A basidiospore germinates to produce a haploid primary _____. │
└────────────────────────────────────────────────────────────────────┘
                                  │
                                  ▼
┌────────────────────────────────────────────────────────────────────┐
│ The mycelia of different mating types fuse to produce a(an) _____. │
└────────────────────────────────────────────────────────────────────┘
                                  │
                                  ▼
┌────────────────────────────────────────────────────────────────────┐
│ A fruiting body pushes above ground, forming a(an) _____ at the soil's surface. │
└────────────────────────────────────────────────────────────────────┘
                                  │
                                  ▼
┌────────────────────────────────────────────────────────────────────┐
│ Two nuclei in each basidium fuse to form a diploid _____. │
└────────────────────────────────────────────────────────────────────┘
                                  │
                                  ▼
┌────────────────────────────────────────────────────────────────────┐
│ Each zygote undergoes meiosis, forming clusters of diploid _____. │
└────────────────────────────────────────────────────────────────────┘
```

The Imperfect Fungi (page 536)

23. The phylum Deuteromycota is composed of what fungi? _____
_____
_____

24. What is *Penicillium notatum*, and where does it grow naturally? _____
_____

25. What is produced from *Penicillium notatum*? _____
_____

Reading Skill Practice

You can often increase your understanding of what you've read by making comparisons. A compare-and-contrast table helps you to do this. On a separate sheet of paper, make a table to compare the four main groups of fungi you read about in Section 21–2. For more information about compare-and-contrast tables, see Organizing Information in Appendix A of your textbook.

Section 21-3 Ecology of Fungi (pages 537-542)

Key Concepts
- What is the main role of fungi in natural ecosystems?
- What problems do parasitic fungi cause?
- What kinds of symbiotic relationships do fungi form with other organisms?

All Fungi Are Heterotrophs (page 537)

1. Fungi cannot manufacture their own food because they are _____.

2. What are saprobes? _____

_____

_____

Fungi as Decomposers (page 538)

3. Fungi recycle nutrients breaking down the bodies and wastes of other _____.

4. How do fungi break down leaves, fruit, and other organic material into simple

molecules? _____

_____

_____

Fungi as Parasites (pages 538-539)

5. Parasitic fungi cause serious plant and animal _____.

6. Circle the letter of each example of a fungal plant disease.

   a. wheat rust   **b.** corn smut   **c.** thrush   **d.** mildews

7. Rusts are members of the phylum _____.

8. What two kinds of plants do wheat rusts need to complete their life cycle?

_____

_____

_____

9. One deuteromycete can infect the areas between the human toes, causing an infection

known as _____.

10. What happens when the fungus that causes athlete's foot infects other areas of the

body? _____

_____

Symbiotic Relationships (pages 540–542)

11. Lichens and mycorrhizae are both examples of what kind of symbiotic relationship?

_____

12. What are lichens? _____

_____

13. What is the photosynthetic organism in a lichen? _____

_____

14. Where do lichens grow? _____

_____

15. What benefits do the fungus and the photosynthetic organism derive from the association in a lichen? _____

_____

_____

16. What are mycorrhizae? _____

17. Why is the presence of mycorrhizae essential for the growth of many plants?

_____

_____

Chapter 21 Fungi
Vocabulary Review

Matching   *In the space provided, write the letter that best matches each term.*

_____ **1.** spore

_____ **2.** rhizoids

_____ **3.** stolons

_____ **4.** gametangia

_____ **5.** zygospore

_____ **6.** sporangiophore

_____ **7.** sporangium

a. spores are produced in these sructures

b. a rootlike hypha found in fungi

c. a haploid reproductive cell

d. gamete-forming structures

e. a resting spore that contains zygotes

f. stemlike hyphae that are found on the surface

g. specialized hyphae where sporangia are found

Completion   *Fill in the blanks with terms from Chapter 21.*

8. Multicellular fungi are composed of thin filaments called _____.

9. The bodies of multicellular fungi are composed of many hyphae tangled together into a thick mass called a(an) _____.

10. A(An) _____ body is a fungal reproductive structure growing from the mycelium.

11. The process of asexual reproduction in yeasts is called _____.

12. The spore-bearing structure of a club fungus is called the _____.

13. The phylum composed of fungi that have never been observed to have a sexual phase in their life cycles is the _____ fungi.

14. Organisms that obtain food from decaying organic matter are called _____.

15. A(An) _____ is a symbiotic association between a fungus and a photosynthetic organism.

Chapter 21 Fungi   **Section Review 21-1**

Reviewing Key Concepts

Multiple Choice *On the lines provided, write the answer that best completes the sentence or answers the question.*

_____ 1. Which term describes the cells of fungi?
   a. prokaryotic   c. protistlike
   b. eukaryotic   d. phototropic

_____ 2. Which term best describes how fungi obtain energy?
   a. phototrophic   c. autotrophic
   b. chemoautotrophic   d. heterotrophic

_____ 3. Fungi have cell walls composed of
   a. hyphae.   c. chitin.
   b. sporangia.   d. mycelium.

_____ 4. The body of a multicellular fungus is composed of a
   mass of hyphae called a
   a. mycelium.   c. sporangia.
   b. gametangium.   d. spore.

_____ 5. How do most fungi reproduce?
   a. only sexually   c. both sexually and asexually
   b. only asexually   d. fungi do not reproduce

Identifying Structures *On the lines provided, identify the structures of a multicellular fungus as one of the following:* fruiting body, hyphae, *or* mycelium.

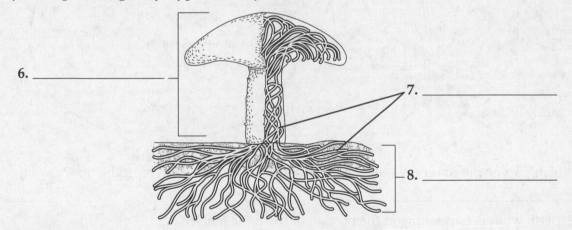

6. _____

7. _____

8. _____

Reviewing Key Skills

9. **Comparing and Contrasting** How are asexual and sexual reproduction in fungi different?

_____

_____

10. **Applying Concepts** Describe three ways that fungi have adapted to increase the successful distribution of spores.

_____

_____

Reviewing Key Concepts

Matching *On the lines provided, match each phylum with its description. A letter may be used more than once.*

_____ 1. The life cycles of these fungi include a zygospore.

_____ 2. Sexual reproduction involves the formation of an ascus.

_____ 3. This phylum has a specialized reproductive structure that resembles a club.

_____ 4. The reproductive structure is called a basidium.

_____ 5. Fungi in this phylum do not appear to have a sexual phase in their life cycles.

a. Zygomycetes
b. Basidiomycetes
c. Deuteromycetes
d. Ascomycetes

Reviewing Key Skills

Interpreting Graphics *Use the diagram to answer the following questions on the life cycle of a zygomycete.*

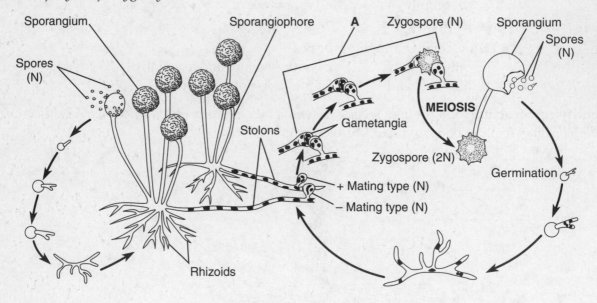

6. Which part of the diagram—the left or the right—shows asexual reproduction?

_____

7. Explain what is happening in the portion of the cycle labeled A.

_____

_____

_____

8. Three specialized types of hyphae are shown in the diagram. Name each one and describe its function.

_____

_____

_____

Chapter 21 Fungi **Section Review 21-3**

Reviewing Key Concepts

Short Answer *On the lines provided, answer the following questions.*

1. What role do fungi play as decomposers in ecosystems?

   _____

   _____

2. Give an example of a plant disease caused by a parasitic fungus. How does
   the fungus affect the plant?

   _____

   _____

3. Give an example of a human disease caused by fungal parasites. How does
   the fungus affect a person?

   _____

   _____

4. Why are lichens considered to be a symbiotic association between two organisms?

   _____

   _____

5. What are mycorrhizae and why is the association important to many ecosystems?

   _____

   _____

Reviewing Key Skills

Interpreting Graphics *On the lines provided, label the structures that make up a
lichen as one of the following:* Densely packed hyphae, Layer of algae or
cyanobacteria, *and* Loosely packed hyphae. *A structure can be used more than once.*

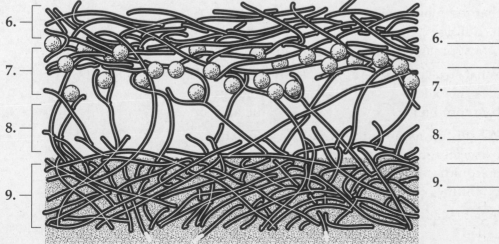

6. _____

7. _____

8. _____

9. _____

Matching *On the lines provided, write the letter of the definition that best matches each term on the left.*

_____ **1.** hyphae

_____ **2.** chitin

_____ **3.** mycelium

_____ **4.** sporangium

_____ **5.** sporangiophore

_____ **6.** gametangium

_____ **7.** rhizoid

_____ **8.** stolon

_____ **9.** zygospore

_____ **10.** conidia

a. rootlike hypha that penetrates food surfaces

b. stemlike hypha that runs along food surfaces

c. complex carbohydrate found in cell walls of fungi

d. structure in which spores are produced

e. thick mass of hyphae

f. tiny spores formed at the tips of specialized hyphae called conidiophores

g. contains zygotes formed during the sexual phase of the mold's life cycle

h. specialized hypha that ends in a sporangium

i. thin filaments that make up multicellular fungi

j. gamete-forming structure

Multiple Choice *On the lines provided, write the letter of the answer that best completes the sentence or answers the question.*

_____ **11.** What is the name of the reproductive structure in ascomycetes that contains spores?
   a. sporangium   c. conidium
   b. ascus   d. basidium

_____ **12.** In ascomycetes, the eight cells produced after meiosis and mitosis are known as
   a. ascospores.   c. basidia.
   b. conidium.   d. gametangia.

_____ **13.** In basidiomycetes, what is the reproductive structure that resembles a club called?
   a. a stolon   c. a basidium
   b. a sporangiophore   d. an ascospore

_____ **14.** What structure forms at the edge of a basidium?
   a. a rhizoid   c. a basidiospore
   b. a conidium   d. a gametangium

_____ **15.** What is the name of the symbiotic association between a fungus and a photosynthetic organism?
   a. conidia   c. stolon
   b. chitin   d. lichen

_____ **16.** What is the association of a plant root and a fungus called?
   a. gametangium   c. sporangiophore
   b. mycorrhiza   d. rhizoid

Name_____ Class_____ Date _____

Labeling Diagrams *On the lines provided, label the different parts of the diagram of the bread mold below.*

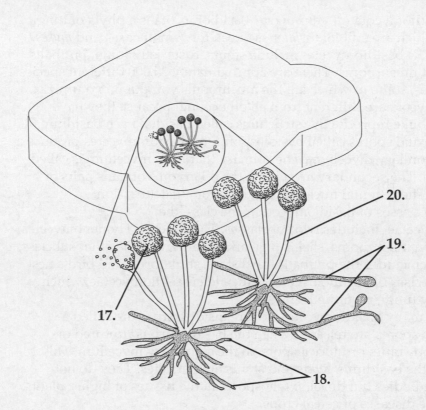

17. _____
18. _____
19. _____
20. _____

Basidiomycota on Your Pizza?

Do you like Basidiomycota on your pizza? Basidiomycota is a phyla of fungi, some types of which are edible. *Basidion* is Greek for "small base" and *mykes* means fungus. The basidiomycetes include smuts, rusts, jelly fungi, puffballs, stinkhorns—and mushrooms. There are approximately 25,000 different species of basidiomycetes, some of which are the mushrooms you put on your pizza.

The Basidiomycota are different from all other fungi because they have microscopic, clublike reproductive structures called basidia. Each basidium bears haploid sexual spores called basidiospores. All basidiomycetes produce a primary and secondary mycelium. The primary (haploid) mycelium is called the monokaryon. The secondary mycelium, the dikaryon, contains pairs of parental nuclei. The parental nuclei replicate by conjugate division.

There are two classes of basidiomycetes. One class, the Homobasidiomycetae, includes two subclasses. The subclass Hymenomycetes includes common mushrooms, shelf fungi, and coral fungi. The other subclass, Gasteromycetes, includes the puffballs, earthstars, stinkhorns, and bird's nest fungi. The other class of basidiomycetes is the Heterbasidiomycetae, which includes the jelly fungi, rusts, and smuts.

The spores of many basidiomycetes mature inside a structure called a basidiocarp. The spores are released when the basidiocarp is ruptured or decays. Rusts and smuts produce a spore on the secondary mycelium. This spore produces the basidium. Rusts and smuts are parasites. They do not produce fruiting bodies but develop teliospores in the tissues of higher plants. Some rusts cause diseases of cereal crops.

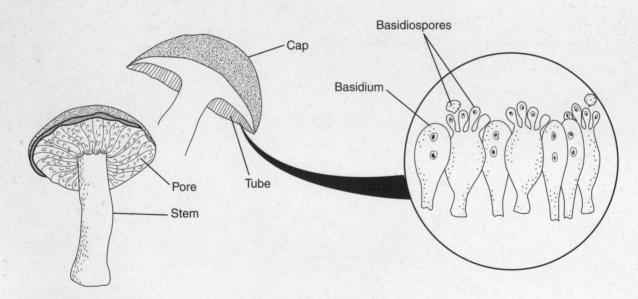

Evaluation *Answer the following questions on a separate sheet of paper.*

1. What makes basidiomycetes unique from other fungi?

2. Look at the illustration above, which shows reproduction of the mushroom *Boletus chrysenteron.* Write a paragraph that discusses reproduction in basidiomycetes.

Name_____ Class_____ Date _____

Chapter 21 Fungi   Graphic Organizer

Concept Map

Using information from the chapter, complete the concept map below. If there is not enough room in the concept map to write your answers, write them on a separate sheet of paper.

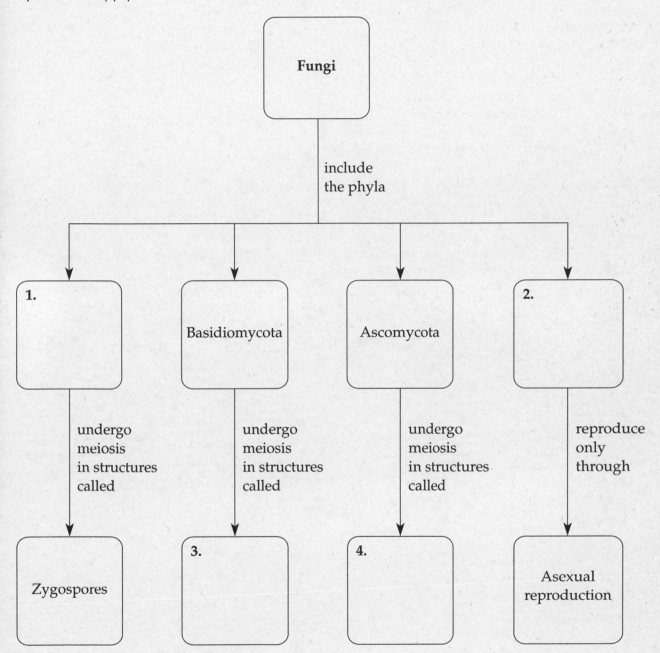

Chapter 21 Fungi   **Chapter Test A**

Multiple Choice

Write the letter that best answers the question or completes the statement on the line provided.

_____ 1. Fungi do NOT
   a. carry out photosynthesis.
   b. grow on their food source.
   c. digest food outside their bodies.
   d. absorb food through their cell walls.

_____ 2. The tangled mass that makes up the body of a fungus is the
   a. hypha.   c. mycelium.
   b. rhizoid.   d. stolon.

_____ 3. Sporangia are found at the tops of specialized hyphae called
   a. sporangiophores.   c. gametangia.
   b. mycelia.   d. stolons.

_____ 4. *Rhizopus* reproduces
   a. by sexual reproduction only.
   b. by asexual reproduction only.
   c. by both asexual and sexual reproduction.
   d. all of the above

_____ 5. In the life cycle of molds, when hyphae of different mating types meet, each hypha forms a
   a. sporangium.   c. zygospore.
   b. zoospore.   d. gametangium.

_____ 6. The dry, powdered yeast used to bake bread actually contains
   a. zygospores.   c. conidia.
   b. ascospores.   d. sporangia.

_____ 7. In mushrooms, the basidia are found on the
   a. base.   c. cap.
   b. stalk.   d. root.

_____ 8. Over time, nutrients at the center of a large mycelium become depleted, causing new mushrooms to sprout only
   a. in a cluster at the center.
   b. in a ring at the outer edges.
   c. when the nutrients are replaced.
   d. after budding takes place.

_____ 9. *Penicillium* reproduces asexually by means of conidia, similar to reproduction in a(an)
   a. ascomycete.   c. basidiomycete.
   b. zygomycete.   d. lichen.

____**10.** Fungi that absorb food from decaying organic matter are
     a. parasites.   c. mutualists.
     b. saprobes.   d. autotrophs.

____**11.** Fungi feed on
     a. only living organisms.
     b. only dead organisms.
     c. both living and dead organisms.
     d. only other fungi.

____**12.** Crop damage by fungal diseases is
     a. greatest in tropical areas.
     b. least in tropical areas.
     c. greatest in temperate areas.
     d. not affected by climate.

____**13.** The fungus that forms a mycelium within the outer layers of
human skin causes
     a. ringworm and athlete's foot.
     b. thrush and reproductive-tract infections.
     c. reproductive-tract infections and ringworm.
     d. athlete's foot and thrush.

____**14.** Which statement about lichens is correct?
     a. They are not tolerant of harsh conditions.
     b. They cannot make their own food.
     c. They grow only in soil.
     d. They are composed of an alga or a cyanobacterium and a
         fungus living together.

____**15.** The association of plants and fungi in mycorrhizae illustrates
a type of relationship called
     a. parasitism.   c. competition.
     b. mutualism.   d. parallelism.

Completion

Complete each statement on the line provided.

16. The cell walls of fungi are composed of the carbohydrate _____ .

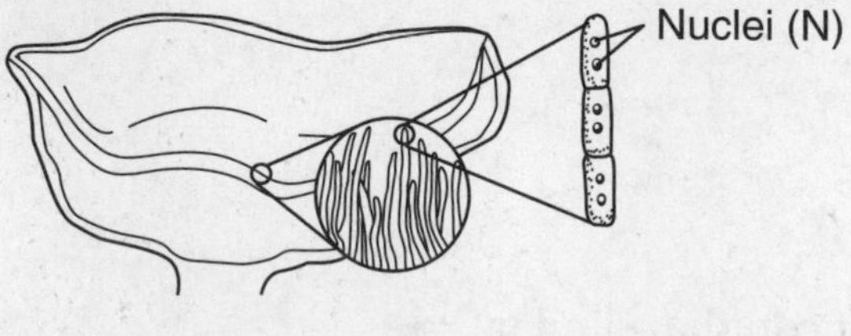

Nuclei (N)

Figure 1

17. In the _____ stage of the ascomycete life cycle, shown in Figure 1, cells
contain two nuclei.

Name ______________________ Class ________________ Date ______________

18. The basidiospores of ________________ fungi are scattered by the wind.

19. Fungi break down complex organic matter by releasing digestive ________________.

20. A serious fungal disease of ________________ needs two different plants to complete its life cycle.

Short Answer

In complete sentences, write the answers to the questions on the lines provided.

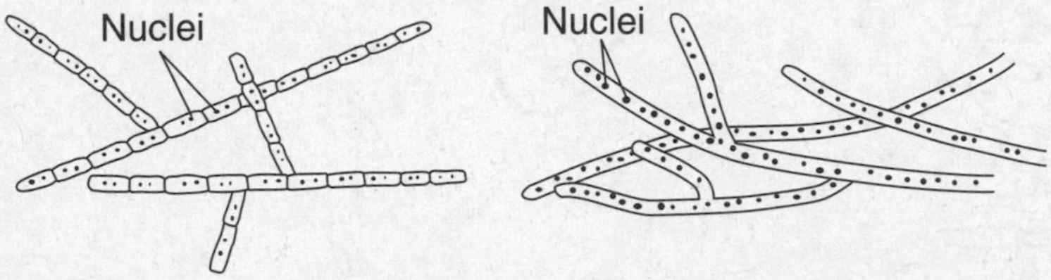

Figure 2

21. How do the two types of hyphae shown in Figure 2 differ?

22. What three functions do rhizoids serve in bread mold?

23. Suppose you like mushrooms and saw some growing in a yard. Would you pick and eat them? Why or why not?

24. What is the most important role of fungi in natural ecosystems, and why is this role important?

25. How do lichens encourage soil formation on barren rock?

Using Science Skills

Use the diagram below to answer the following questions on the lines provided.

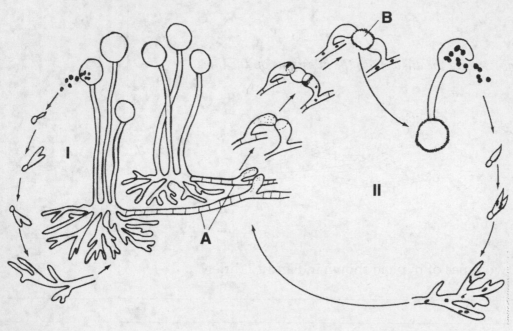

Figure 3

26. **Inferring** What mating type or types are labeled A in Figure 3?

_____

_____

27. **Predicting** Predict what would happen to the structure labeled B in Figure 3 if conditions were not favorable for reproduction.

_____

_____

_____

28. **Classifying** To what phylum does the organism shown in Figure 3 belong?

_____

29. **Interpreting Graphics** Which section of Figure 3, I or II, shows sexual reproduction?

_____

30. **Applying Concepts** Identify the structure labeled B in Figure 3 and explain how it is analogous to a fertilized animal egg.

_____

_____

_____

Essay

Write the answer to each question in the space provided.

31. Does the haploid or diploid condition occur most in the life cycle of fungi? Explain your answer.

32. Name the four phyla of fungi. What characteristic determines the phylum into which a fungus is placed?

33. Describe the fruiting body of a mushroom. What allows a mushroom to develop so quickly that it can spring up overnight?

34. How are fungi both helpful and harmful to people?

35. Why is it not beneficial to kill all bacteria on and in the body, and what is a common result of killing naturally occurring bacteria?

Multiple Choice

Write the letter that best answers the question or completes the statement on the line provided.

_____ 1. All fungi
   a. make their food.
   b. absorb their food.
   c. produce mushrooms.

_____ 2. A mushroom is a fungal
   a. fruiting body.
   b. lichen.
   c. mycorrhiza.

_____ 3. Most fungi reproduce
   a. asexually only.
   b. sexually only.
   c. both sexually and asexually.

_____ 4. Stinkhorns, which mimic the odor of rotting meat, have spores that are dispersed by
   a. wind.
   b. birds.
   c. flies.

_____ 5. Dark fuzz that grows on bread is an example of
   a. a toadstool.
   b. a spore.
   c. mold.

_____ 6. Bread rises because fermentation by yeast produces
   a. spores.
   b. rhizoids.
   c. carbon dioxide.

_____ 7. Mushrooms are classified as
   a. common molds.
   b. sac fungi.
   c. club fungi.

_____ 8. Which structure is NOT found in a mushroom?
   a. ascus
   b. gills
   c. cap

____ 9. Which statement about *Penicillium* is correct?
    a. It produces mushrooms.
    b. It causes bread to rise.
    c. It is the source of an antibiotic.

____10. An important role of fungi in an ecosystem is
    a. photosynthesis.
    b. breaking down dead organisms.
    c. making alcohol.

____11. Fungi might have been important to the evolution of
    a. worms.
    b. grasshoppers.
    c. plants.

____12. The human disease ringworm is caused by
    a. worms.
    b. bacteria.
    c. a fungus.

____13. The growth of yeasts in moist regions of the body is kept in check by competition from
    a. antibiotics.
    b. bacteria.
    c. rusts.

____14. The normal balance between bacteria and yeasts in the body can be upset by
    a. eating yeast-leavened bread.
    b. eating edible mushrooms.
    c. using antibiotics.

____15. Which of the following is NOT a single organism?
    a. rust
    b. yeast
    c. lichen

Completion

Complete each statement on the line provided.

16. _____ reproduction takes place when cells or hyphae break off a fungus and begin to grow.

17. Spore-bearing structures called basidia are found in the _____ of mushrooms.

18. Imperfect fungi do not have a(an) _____ phase in their life cycles.

19. The symbiotic associations of plant roots and fungi are called _____.

Name_____ Class_____ Date _____

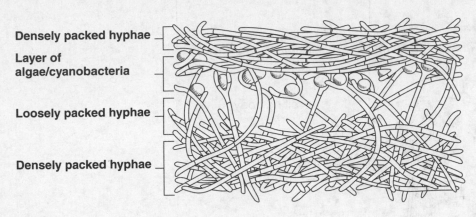

Densely packed hyphae —

Layer of algae/cyanobacteria —

Loosely packed hyphae —

Densely packed hyphae —

Figure 1

20. The cyanobacterium or algal layer of the _____ shown in Figure 1 performs photosynthesis.

Short Answer

In complete sentences, write the answers to the questions on the lines provided.

21. What are the individual threads of a fungus called, and what structure do they form when they appear as a tangled mass?

_____

_____

22. In the ascomycete fruiting body shown in Figure 2, how many nuclei are found in each cell of the hyphae, and what separates each cell of the hyphae?

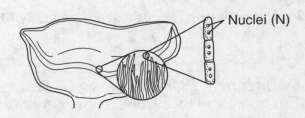

Nuclei (N)

_____

_____

_____

Figure 2

23. Name two commercial uses of yeast.

_____

_____

24. Why are basidiomycetes called club fungi?

_____

_____

25. What is an example of a competition between humans and fungi for nutrients?

_____

_____

Using Science Skills

Use the diagram below to answer the following questions on the lines provided.

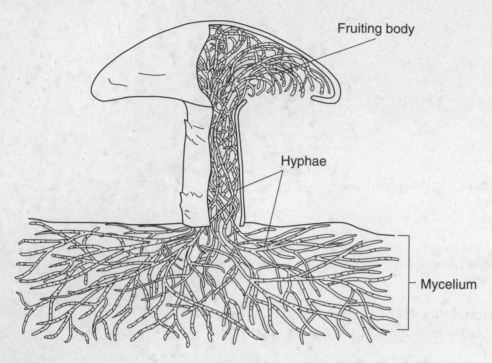

Figure 3

26. **Formulating Hypotheses** How many fungal fruiting bodies are shown in Figure 3?

_____

27. **Interpreting Graphics** According to Figure 3, what does the structure of the below-ground portion of the mycelium have in common with the structure of the fruiting body?

_____

28. **Predicting** Mushrooms sometimes grow from the trunks of trees. Which structure shown in Figure 3 would likely be embedded in the tree's bark?

_____

_____

29. **Inferring** Look at the mycelium shown in Figure 3. Would it be possible to easily detect the presence of a mycelium underground if no fruiting bodies were present? Explain your answer.

_____

30. **Interpreting Graphics** What kind of a structure is the fruiting body shown in Figure 3?

_____

_____

Unit 6 Microorganisms and Fungi   **Unit Test A**

Multiple Choice
Write the letter that best answers the question or completes the statement on the line provided.

_____ 1. Which of the following is NOT a characteristic used to identify prokaryotes?

    a. type of cell wall   c. shape

    b. habitat   d. movement

_____ 2. Which of the following describes binary fission in prokaryotes?

    a. Spores form and then germinate when conditions are good.

    b. Genetic information is exchanged through a hollow bridge.

    c. Gametes from opposite mating types fuse.

    d. A cell replicates its DNA and divides in half.

_____ 3. A typical virus is composed of a

    a. prophage embedded within RNA or DNA.

    b. core of RNA or DNA surrounded by a protein coat.

    c. viroid surrounded by a double helix of DNA.

    d. clump of peptidoglycan within a coat of chitin.

_____ 4. The process in which the host cell makes copies of a virus indefinitely is called a(an)

    a. lysogenic infection.

    b. algal bloom.

    c. lytic infection.

    d. alternation of generations.

_____ 5. Which of the following is a disease caused by a bacterium?

    a. tuberculosis   c. hepatitis C

    b. common cold   d. warts

_____ 6. Which of the following is NOT a protist?

    a. amoeba

    b. paramecium

    c. mushroom

    d. Euglena

_____ 7. Accessory pigments allow many algae to absorb

    a. nutrients from decaying organic matter.

    b. chlorophyll *a* during photosynthesis.

    c. light at different wavelengths other than chlorophyll.

    d. delicate cell walls rich in silicon.

____ **8.** Euglenophytes are like zooflagellates in that members of both groups
   a. are green and contain chloroplasts.
   b. move and feed using cilia.
   c. are autotrophs that carry out photosynthesis.
   d. swim using flagella.

____ **9.** The largest known alga is giant kelp, which is an example of
   a. red algae.
   b. green algae.
   c. brown algae.
   d. yellow algae.

____ **10.** The plasmodium of an acellular slime mold is a
   a. single-celled phase of the organism's life cycle.
   b. single structure with many nuclei.
   c. colony of filaments in which cells are stacked.
   d. thick mass of hyphae tangled together.

____ **11.** All fungi are eukaryotic
   a. autotrophs.
   b. chemoautotrophs.
   c. parasites.
   d. heterotrophs.

____ **12.** Molds seem to spring up in many different locations because
   a. most fungi reproduce sexually.
   b. fungal spores are found in almost every environment.
   c. fungi lack membrane-bound organelles.
   d. most molds are obligate anaerobes.

____ **13.** The process of asexual reproduction in yeasts is called
   a. budding.
   b. basidia.
   c. conjugation.
   d. alternation of generations.

____ **14.** Organisms that obtain food from decaying organic matter are
   a. autotrophs.   c. parasites.
   b. sporangia.   d. saprobes.

____ **15.** The green alga or cyanobacterium in a lichen provides the fungus with
   a. water and minerals collected from the environment.
   b. protection from water molds and other pathogens.
   c. a source of energy through photosynthesis.
   d. shade and protection from intense sunlight.

Name_____ Class_____ Date _____

Completion
Complete each statement on the line provided.

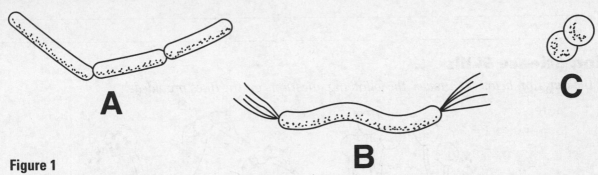

Figure 1

16. The bacteria labeled C in Figure 1 are examples of _____.

17. Viruses that contain RNA as their genetic information are called

    _____.

18. A(An) _____ is a preparation of weakened or killed pathogens used to prompt the body to produce immunity to a disease.

19. The population of small, photosynthetic organisms found near the surface of oceans is called _____.

20. *Penicillium notatum*, which has never been observed to reproduce sexually, is classified as a(an) _____ fungus.

Short Answer
In complete sentences, write the answers to the questions on the lines provided.

21. In what ways are archaebacteria different from eubacteria?

    _____

    _____

22. Why can't viral diseases be treated with antibiotics?

    _____

    _____

    _____

23. What characteristics do plants and green algae share?

    _____

    _____

    _____

24. What is alternation of generations?

    _____

    _____

    _____

25. How do fungi help maintain equilibrium in ecosystems?

_____

_____

_____

Using Science Skills

Use the diagram below to answer the following questions on the lines provided.

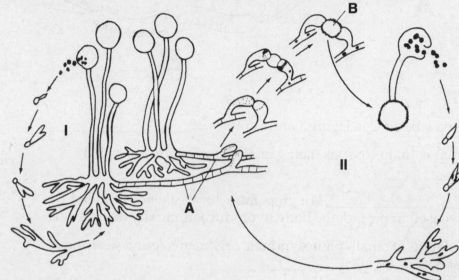

Figure 2

26. Classifying Identify the organism whose life cycle is illustrated in Figure 2.

_____

_____

27. Interpreting Graphics Explain in general terms what Figure 2 depicts, including labels for section I and section II.

_____

_____

28. Interpreting Graphics What are the two structures labeled A in Figure 2, and how are they involved in reproduction?

_____

_____

29. Interpreting Graphics What is the structure labeled B in Figure 2? Explain how that structure became either haploid or diploid.

_____

_____

30. Applying Concepts What follows the formation of structure B in the life cycle of this organism, and what is that step's significance for the organism's survival?

_____

_____

Essay

Write the answer to each question in the space provided.

31. Describe the structure of a typical eubacterium.

32. Describe what occurs in a lytic infection.

33. Identify the cause of malaria, and explain how it is spread.

34. Describe the structure of a typical multicellular fungus.

35. What are mycorrhizae, and why are they essential for the growth of many plants?

Unit 6 Microorganisms and Fungi   Unit Test B

Multiple Choice

Write the letter that best answers the question or completes the statement on the line provided.

_____ 1. What are the two kingdoms of prokaryotes?

    a. monera and bacteria

    b. eubacteria and archaebacteria

    c. eubacteria and monera

_____ 2. In the process of binary fission, a bacterium

    a. forms an endospore and waits for favorable conditions.

    b. replicates its DNA and divides in half.

    c. forms a hollow bridge to another bacterium.

_____ 3. A virus's protein coat is called its

    a. prophage.

    b. rhizoid.

    c. capsid.

_____ 4. What is a pathogen?

    a. a virus that infects bacteria

    b. a bacterium undergoing conjugation

    c. a disease-causing agent

_____ 5. Which of the following is a disease caused by a bacterium?

    a. AIDS

    b. strep throat

    c. common cold

_____ 6. Eukaryotes that are not plants, animals, or fungi are classified as

    a. protists.

    b. heterotrophs.

    c. prokaryotes.

_____ 7. The sporozoan *Plasmodium* causes the disease called

    a. tuberculosis.

    b. athlete's foot.

    c. malaria.

_____ 8. What allows algae to harvest and use the energy from sunlight?

    a. chlorophyll and accessory pigments

    b. cell walls rich in silicon

    c. alternation of generations

_____ 9. A haploid reproductive cell is called a(an)

  a. gamete.

  b. trichocyst.

  c. spore.

_____ 10. What is an algal bloom?

  a. a plasmodium of an acellular slime mold

  b. an enormous mass of algae

  c. a clump of accessory pigments

_____ 11. Eukaryotic heterotrophs that have cell walls are known as

  a. bacteria.

  b. water molds.

  c. fungi.

_____ 12. What are rhizoids?

  a. the accessory pigments found in red algae

  b. the rootlike hyphae of bread molds that penetrate the bread's surface

  c. hairlike projections similar to flagella

_____ 13. The unicellular fungi used for baking and brewing are the

  a. common yeasts.

  b. water molds.

  c. chrysophytes.

_____ 14. The mushroom seen above ground is the organism's

  a. mycelium.

  b. fruiting body.

  c. plasmodium.

_____ 15. Mycorrhizae are mutualistic relationships between

  a. bacteria and viroids.

  b. fungi and algae.

  c. plant roots and fungi.

Completion

Complete each statement on the line provided.

16. Scientists think that _____ may be ancestors of eukaryotes.

17. Compounds that block the growth and reproduction of bacteria are called _____.

18. Amoebas move via temporary cytoplasmic projections known as _____.

19. Green algae share many characteristics with _____, including their photosynthetic pigments and cell wall composition.

20. Multicellular fungi are composed of thin filaments called _____.

Short Answer

In complete sentences, write the answers to the questions on the lines provided.

21. What are three methods used to control bacterial growth?

_____

_____

_____

22. Describe a typical virus.

_____

_____

23. In your textbook, protists are classified into three groups: animal-like protists, plantlike protists, and funguslike protists. What is the basis for that classification?

_____

_____

24. What is the process of alternation of generations in algae?

_____

_____

_____

25. What are the four main groups of fungi?

_____

_____

_____

_____

Name_____ Class_____ Date_____

Using Science Skills

Use the art below to answer the following questions on the lines provided.

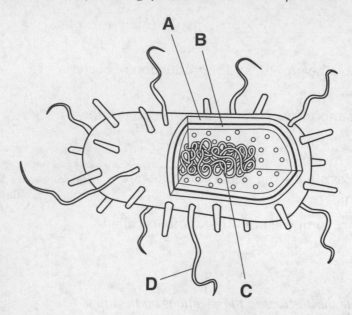

Figure 1

26. **Interpreting Graphics** Is the organism illustrated in Figure 1 unicellular or multicellular?

_____

27. **Inferring** Structure B is a cell membrane. What does structure A represent?

_____

28. **Interpreting Graphics** Structure C is DNA. How is this genetic material found in this organism?

_____

_____

29. **Interpreting Graphics** Structure D is a flagellum. What is the function of that structure?

_____

_____

30. **Classifying** Identify the kind of organism shown in Figure 1. Describe its main characteristics.

_____

_____

_____

ANSWER KEY

Chapter 19 Bacteria and Viruses

Answers for the Adapted Reading and Study Workbook (worksheets pp. 7–13) can be found in the Adapted Reading and Study Workbook, Annotated Teacher's Edition.

Answers for the Adapted Reading and Study Workbook (worksheets pp. 16–25) can be found in the Adapted Reading and Study Workbook, Annotated Teacher's Edition.

Section Review 19-1

1. Archaebacteria lack the peptidoglycan of eubacteria and also have different membrane lipids. Also, DNA sequences of key archaebacterial genes are more like those of eukaryotes than those of eubacteria. **2.** Prokaryotes are identified by their shapes (rod, spherical, or spiral), the chemical nature of their cell walls, the way they move, and the way they obtain energy. **3.** Some are producers that capture energy by photosynthesis. Others are decomposers. Still other bacteria have human uses. **4.** cell wall **5.** DNA **6.** pili **7.** flagellum **8.** The bacterium is a bacillus because it is rod shaped. **9.** This bacterium moves by using its flagella. **10.** In binary fission, a bacterium replicates its DNA and divides in half; there is no exchange or recombination of genetic information. In conjugation, a hollow bridge forms between two bacterial cells, and genes move from one cell to the other.

Section Review 19-2

1. d **2.** d **3.** c **4.** a **5.** The bacteriophage injects DNA into a bacterium. **6.** The bacteriophage DNA forms a circle. **7.** The bacteriophage takes over the bacterium's metabolism, causing synthesis of new bacteriophage proteins and nucleic acids. **8.** Bacteriophage proteins and nucleic acids assemble into complete bacteriophage particles. **9.** Bacteriophage enzyme lyses the bacterium's cell wall, releasing new bacteriophage particles that can attack other cells. **10.** Viruses are not considered to be living things because they aren't made up of cells and can't reproduce independently.

Section Review 19-3

1. tissues **2.** toxins **3.** pathogen **4.** sterilization **5.** vaccine **6.** Both tuberculosis and strep throat are caused by bacteria. However, the bacteria that cause tuberculosis break down lung tissue, whereas the bacteria that cause strep throat release toxins into the bloodstream. **7.** Antibiotics are compounds that block the growth and reproduction of bacteria; they have no effect on viruses. **8.** Both antibiotics and disinfectants kill bacteria. Antibiotics are compounds used to kill bacteria in an organism, whereas disin-fectants are chemical solutions used to kill bacteria on surfaces. **9.** Cooking meats until they are well done raises the temperature of the meat to a point where bacteria are killed. **10.** Both viroids and prions are viruslike particles that cause disease. Viroids are single-stranded RNA molecules that attack plants, whereas prions are protein particles that attack animals, including humans.

Chapter Vocabulary Review

1. bacillus **2.** endospore **3.** lysogenic **4.** capsid **5.** virus **6.** (across) chemoautotroph **6.** (down) conjugation **7.** prion **8.** coccus **9.** antibiotic **10.** binary **11.** nitrogen **12.** flagellum **13.** lytic **14.** prokaryote **15.** pathogen **16.** eubacteria **17.** archaebacteria **18.** spirillum **19.** flagellum **20.** photoautotroph **21.** photoheterotroph **22.** aerobes **23.** anaerobes **24.** facultative **25.** decomposers **26.** virus **27.** bacteriophage **28.** retrovirus **29.** antibiotic **30.** sterilization

Enrichment

1. Acid-fast bacteria are characterized by a high lipid content. They are resistant to Gram staining, but are identifiable by an acid-fast stain test. **2.** All the bacteria in the sample will be covered with dye and appear to be stained. However, only the acid-fast bacteria have absorbed the dye. When the sample is washed, the dye that covers the bacteria is removed while the dye that has been absorbed remains. This leaves the acid-fast bacteria clearly visible.

Graphic Organizer

1. Way they move **2.** Way they obtain energy **3.** Cocci **4.** Spirilla **5.** Heterotrophs **6.** Photoautotrophs **7.** Chemoheterotrophs

Chapter 19—Test A

Multiple Choice 1. D **2.** A **3.** D **4.** C **5.** A **6.** B **7.** D **8.** B **9.** A **10.** B **11.** C **12.** B **13.** A **14.** A **15.** B **Completion 16.** bacillus (rod-shaped bacteria) **17.** nitrogen fixation **18.** prophage **19.** head **20.** DNA **Short Answer 21.** Prokaryotes are identified by (1) their shape, (2) the chemical nature of their cell walls, (3) the way they move, and (4) the way they obtain energy. **22.** Accept any two of the following roles: carrying out photosynthesis, performing nitrogen fixation, decomposing dead matter and recycling nutrients. **23.** A virus is a particle of nucleic acid, protein, and, in some cases, lipids that can reproduce only by infecting living cells. A typical virus is composed of a core of either DNA or RNA surrounded by a protein coat called a capsid.

© Pearson Education, Inc., publishing as Pearson Prentice Hall.

145

24. Living things are made up of cells, and they are able to live independently. Viruses are not cellular and must infect a living cell to reproduce. Also, unlike cells, viruses don't grow and develop, don't obtain and use energy, and don't respond to the environment. **25.** Three methods used to control bacteria growth are sterilization by heat, use of disinfectants, and correct food storage and processing. **Using Science Skills 26.** Sample answer: The student has controlled all the variables except the solution that each disk is soaked in. She is probably trying to test the effectiveness of different disinfectants against *E. coli* bacteria. **27.** The disk soaked in distilled water is the control. **28.** Sample answer: The student can measure the width of the area around each disk where bacteria have not grown to determine the effectiveness of the solution in which each disk was soaked. **29.** Disinfectant 1 shows the largest area where growth has been inhibited; thus, it is the most effective disinfectant tested against *E. coli* growth. **30.** Sample answer: Disinfectants act differently to combat bacterial growth. Some disinfectants are more effective at controlling one species of bacteria than another. **Essay 31.** Although eubacteria and archaebacteria are both small, have cell walls, and lack nuclei, they differ in the chemical composition of their cell walls and membrane lipids. Archaebacteria also contain key gene sequences that are more like those of eukaryotes than those of eubacteria. Scientists reason from this that archaebacteria may be the ancestors of eukaryotes. **32.** Binary fission is an asexual form of reproduction that occurs in bacteria. When a bacterium has grown so that it has nearly doubled in size, it replicates its DNA and divides in half. In conjugation, a hollow bridge forms between two bacterial cells, and genes move from one cell to another. **33.** In a lytic infection, a bacteriophage injects DNA into a bacterium and takes over the bacterium's metabolism, causing synthesis of new bacteriophage proteins and nucleic acids. Bacteriophage particles assemble within the bacterium and then lyse the bacterial cell wall, causing the bacterium to burst and releasing bacteriophage particles that can attack other cells. In a lysogenic infection, a bacteriophage injects DNA into a bacterium, and the bacteriophage DNA inserts itself into the bacterial chromosomes. The embedded bacteriophage DNA, called a prophage, may replicate with the bacterium for many generations. **34.** Bacteria cause disease in one of two general ways. Some damage the tissues of the infected organism by breaking them down for food. Other bacteria release toxins that harm the body. **35.** Bacterial infections are caused by bacteria either breaking down the body's tissues for food or releasing harmful toxins into the body. A viral infection results when viruses infect body cells, take over their cellular functioning, and begin replicating themselves. In the process, viruses can destroy body cells.

Chapter 19—Test B

Multiple Choice 1. B **2.** C **3.** C **4.** C **5.** C **6.** B **7.** B **8.** B **9.** C **10.** B **11.** C **12.** A **13.** A **14.** A **15.** B **Completion 16.** conjugation **17.** nitrogen fixation **18.** capsid **19.** vaccine **20.** viroids **Short Answer 21.** A: cell wall, B: cell membrane, C: DNA, D: flagellum **22.** The kingdoms are Archaebacteria and Eubacteria. Accept either of the following differences in the two groups: (1) Archaebacteria lack an important carbohydrate found in the cell walls of eubacteria. (2) DNA sequences of key archaebacterial genes are more like those of eukaryotes than those of eubacteria. **23.** A pathogen is a disease-causing agent. **24.** Some bacteria damage the cells and tissues of the infected organism directly by breaking down the cells for food. Other bacteria release toxins that travel throughout the body interfering with the normal activity of the host. **25.** Three methods are sterilization by heat, use of disinfectants, and correct food storage and processing. **Using Science Skills 26.** the lysogenic cycle **27.** during the lytic cycle **28.** E **29.** C **30.** A

Chapter 20 Protists

Answers for the Adapted Reading and Study Workbook (worksheets pp. 51–57) can be found in the Adapted Reading and Study Workbook, Annotated Teacher's Edition.

Answers for the Adapted Reading and Study Workbook (worksheets pp. 60–73) can be found in the Adapted Reading and Study Workbook, Annotated Teacher's Edition.

Section Review 20-1

1. Protists are eukaryotes that are not members of the kingdoms Plantae, Animalia, or Fungi. **2.** A protist cannot be classified as a plant, an animal, a fungus, or prokaryote. **3.** "the very first" **4.** obtain nutrition **5.** animallike **6.** plantlike **7.** external digestion **8.** Organelles in eukaryotes, like mitochondria and chloroplasts, may be descended from prokaryotes that began to live inside larger prokaryotic cells. **9.** Protists are classified by the way they obtain nutrients. This tells us nothing about their evolutionary relationships. Studying DNA may show the evolutionary relationships between protists, permitting a new system of classification. **10.** The word *Protista* comes from words meaning "the very first"; *proto-galaxy* may mean "the very first galaxy."

Section Review 20-2

1. zooflagellates **2.** sporozoans **3.** ciliates **4.** sarcodines **5.** ciliates **6.** The four phyla of animallike protists are distinguished by their means of movement. **7.** Animallike protists cause the diseases malaria, African sleeping sickness, and amebic dysentery. **8.** Both flagella and cilia are used for movement. However, flagella are long whiplike projections whereas cilia are short hairlike projections. **9.** Conjugation is a sexual process in which there is an exchange of genetic material. Conjugation increases genetic diversity. **10.** *Trichonympha*, a zooflagellate, lives within the digestive system of termites. Termites benefit from cellulase, the enzyme termites need to digest cellulose, produced by the *Trichonympha*. **11.** sarcodine **12.** ciliate

Section Review 20-3

1. Chlorophyll and accessory pigments allow algae to collect and use energy from sunlight. **2.** Euglenophytes have two flagella, chloroplasts, and a tough, flexible cell membrane called a pellicle. **3.** Half of dinoflagellates obtain nutrition through photosynthesis; the other half are heterotrophs. **4.** Many species are luminescent **5.** plantlike protists with gold-colored chloroplasts **6.** produce thin, delicate walls rich in silicon **7.** Phytoplankton are at the base of the food chain and provide food for many organisms. Also, phytoplankton carry out about half of the photosynthesis that occurs on Earth. **8.** Algal blooms develop in water in which the amount of waste is excessive. The algal bloom will deplete water of its nutrients and begin to die. Decomposition of the dead algae will rob the water of its oxygen, which may result in the death of fish and invertebrate life.

Section Review 20-4

1. red algae **2.** brown algae **3.** green algae **4.** diploid **5.** diploid **6.** haploid **7.** haploid **8.** haploid **9. a.** Sexual reproduction produces a zygote that can survive being frozen. **b.** Asexual reproduction will allow the algae population to grow quickly during these favorable conditions.

Section Review 20-5

1. d **2.** c **3.** a **4.** b **5.** both **6.** water molds **7.** slime molds **8.** slime molds **9.** Both types of slime molds begin their life cycles as amoeba-like cells. However, the aggregated cells of cellular slime molds remain distinct, whereas the cells of acellular slime molds actually fuse, producing a structure with many nuclei. **10.** Funguslike protists are important recyclers of organic material. Plants benefit when organic materials are recycled and returned to the soil for reuse. However, funguslike protists can cause diseases in plants.

Chapter Vocabulary Review

1. a **2.** b **3.** b **4.** d **5.** d **6.** a **7.** d **8.** b **9.** c **10.** b **11.** b **12.** d **13.** phytoplankton **14.** phycobilins **15.** filaments **16.** alternation of generations **17.** gametophyte **18.** sporophyte **19.** c **20.** e **21.** a **22.** g **23.** d **24.** b **25.** f

Enrichment

1. Shellfish poached from areas unapproved for harvest have not been monitored for toxins and may harm the people who eat them. **2.** During a bloom, algae quickly multiply and the surrounding water becomes densely populated with algae. Organisms that feed on this population might then be able to collect large amounts of algae with less effort.

Graphic Organizer

1. Animallike **2.–4.** Ciliophora, Zoomastigina, Sarcodina **5.–7.** Pyrrophyta, Chrysophyta, Euglenophyta

Chapter 20—Test A

Multiple Choice **1.** D **2.** A **3.** B **4.** C **5.** A **6.** B **7.** C **8.** C **9.** D **10.** B **11.** B **12.** D **13.** C **14.** C **15.** C **Completion** **16.** pseudopods **17.** dinoflagellates **18.** chlorophyll *a* **19.** photosynthesis **20.** oomycetes (or water molds) **Short Answer** **21.** Members of the phylum Sporozoa do not move on their own. **22.** Chlorophyll and accessory pigments allow algae to harvest and use the energy from sunlight. **23.** "Red tides" are algal blooms of the dinoflagellates *Gonyaulax* and *Karenia.* They are dangerous because eating shellfish from water infected with red tide can cause serious illness, paralysis, and even death in humans and fishes. **24.** Both are large multicellular organisms that are so similar they are difficult to tell apart. The sporophyte produces haploid spores, while the gametophyte produces haploid gametes. **25.** Cells of cellular slime molds are separated by cell membranes during every phase of the mold's life cycle. Cells of acellular slime molds fuse to form a large structure with many nuclei. **Using Science Skills** **26.** malaria; the sporozoan *Plasmodium* **27.** Malaria would be most common in environments where the mosquito that carries the protist is common. Some students may know that malaria is common in tropical environments. **28.** A mosquito has picked up the protist and in turn, injected it (in the form of sporozoites) into a human host. The sporozoites have started to grow in the human liver. **29.** The protists infect red blood cells and ultimately cause them to burst, releasing gametes. **30.** Increased symptoms are associated with the period of blood-cell rupture. **Essay** **31.** African sleeping sickness is caused by the animallike protist *Trypanosoma.* The protists are spread through the bite of the tsetse fly. African sleeping sickness is characterized by chills and rashes. If the protist infects nerve cells, it results in severe damage to the nervous system. Some victims lose consciousness, lapsing into a fatal sleep. **32.** A typical euglena is about 50 micrometers in length. Two flagella emerge from a gullet at one end of the organism, and the longer of these spins in a pattern that pulls the organism rapidly through the water. Near the gullet end of the organism is a cluster of reddish pigment known as the eyespot. The euglena is covered by an intricate cell membrane called a pellicle, which is folded into a series of ribbonlike ridges supported by microtubules. **33.** The cells of *Volvox* are arranged in hollow spheres of between 500 to 50,000 cells, each connected to others by strands of cytoplasm. *Volvox* colonies can coordinate their movement with some cells using their flagella to push while others pull. Most cells in a *Volvox* colony are identical—except for a few gamete-producing cells specialized for reproduction. *Ulva*, on the other hand, is composed of several specialized cell types. For example, some cells form a structure called a holdfast, which attaches the alga to a rock. **34.** During much of their life cycle, cellular slime molds are unicellular and both their appearance and behavior are similar to that of animallike protists. When they aggregate, however, cellular slime molds act like multicellular organisms—they migrate together and produce a single fruiting body as if they were a single organism. **35.** Ecosystems would be littered with the bodies of dead animals and plants. Materials would remain tied up in dead bodies and would not reenter the ecosystem to be used by other living things. Some students may further predict that eventually raw materials for new living things might be depleted to the extent that no more new living things could be produced, and life on Earth would end.

Chapter 20—Test B

Multiple Choice **1.** B **2.** C **3.** A **4.** B **5.** B **6.** C **7.** B **8.** A **9.** A **10.** C **11.** C **12.** B **13.** A **14.** A **15.** A **Completion** **16.** protists **17.** malaria **18.** red blood **19.** sunlight **20.** heterotrophs **Short Answer** **21.** *Trichonympha* breaks down the cellulose in wood, making it possible for termites to eat wood. **22.** Unicellular algae make up a portion of the phytoplankton—the population of small, photosynthetic organisms found near the surface of the ocean. **23.** Accept answers such as: to produce chemicals that are used to maintain proper health and to produce chemicals used in industry (plastics, waxes, transistors, deodorants, paints, lubricants, artificial wood). **24.** funguslike protists that play key roles in recycling organic material **25.** The water mold

Phytophthora infestans infected and destroyed the potato crops in Ireland. **Using Science Skills** **26.** a single-celled organism **27.** Structure A traps food particles in the organism's environment, allowing them to enter the organism's body. **28.** Excess water likely would build up inside the organism. **29.** Structure C is a "working library" of genetic information, which contains multiple copies of most of the genes that the organism uses for its day-to-day existence. **30.** The organism likely could not move normally through its environment.

Chapter 21 Fungi

Answers for the Adapted Reading and Study Workbook (worksheets pp. 99–104) can be found in the Adapted Reading and Study Workbook, Annotated Teacher's Edition.

Answers for the Adapted Reading and Study Workbook (worksheets pp. 107–116) can be found in the Adapted Reading and Study Workbook, Annotated Teacher's Edition.

Section Review 21-1

1. b **2.** d **3.** c **4.** a **5.** c **6.** fruiting body **7.** hyphae **8.** mycelium **9.** Asexual reproduction in fungi takes place when cells or hyphae break off and begin to grow on their own. Some fungi scatter spores that form new fungi. In contrast, sexual reproduction occurs when a plus and a minus hypha both form a gametangium, which fuse together to form zygote nuclei. **10.** One way that fungi have adapted to increase the distribution of spores is by producing a vast quantity of spores, which increases the chances that some will be successful. Some fungi are specialized to attract insects and animals to spread the spores, and still other fungi scatter spores by wind.

Section Review 21-2

1. a **2.** d **3.** b **4.** b **5.** c **6.** The part of the cycle on the left-hand side is asexual reproduction. **7.** In section A, gametangia from the two mating types are fusing to form a zygospore. **8.** The three types of hyphae are rhizoids, which anchor the fungus; stolons, which run along the surface and give rise to the two mating types; and sporangiophores, which give rise at their tips to sporangia, which produce spores.

Section Review 21-3

1. As decomposers, fungi recycle nutrients by breaking down the bodies and wastes of other organisms. **2.** Possible student answer: One plant disease caused by a fungus is corn smut. This fungus destroys the kernels of the corn plant. **3.** Possible student answer: Athlete's foot is a human disease caused by parasitic fungi. It causes a red, inflamed sore on a person's foot. **4.** Lichens are considered a symbiotic association because the fungus and photosynthetic organism that make up lichens live in an association that benefits each organism. **5.** Mycorrhizae are associations of plant roots and fungi. The fungi in the mycorrhizae enable the host plant to absorb more water and nutrients. In turn, the plant provides the fungi with the products of photosynthesis. Many plants are unable to survive without these fungal symbionts. **6.** Densely packed hyphae **7.** Layer of algae or cyanobacteria **8.** Loosely packed hyphae **9.** Densely packed hyphae

Chapter Vocabulary Review
1. i **2.** c **3.** e **4.** d **5.** h **6.** j **7.** a **8.** b **9.** g **10.** f **11.** b **12.** a **13.** c **14.** c **15.** d **16.** b **17.** sporangium **18.** rhizoids **19.** stolons **20.** sporangiophore

Enrichment
1. Basidiomycetes are unique from other fungi because they have microscopic, clublike reproductive structures called basidia. **2.** Possible student answer: The basidiomycota have microscopic, clublike reproductive structures called basidia. Each basidium bears haploid sexual spores, called basidiospores. All basidiomycetes produce a primary and secondary mycelium. The primary (haploid) mycelium is called the monokaryon. The secondary mycelium, the dikaryon, contains pairs of parental nuclei. The parental nuclei replicate by conjugate division. The spores that are produced mature in a structure called a basidiocarp, which then releases the spores. The spores will mature into a new organism if environmental conditions are correct.

Graphic Organizer
1. Zygomycota **2.** Deuteromycota **3.** Basidia **4.** Asci

Chapter 21—Test A
Multiple Choice **1.** A **2.** C **3.** A **4.** C **5.** D **6.** B **7.** C **8.** B **9.** A **10.** B **11.** C **12.** A **13.** A **14.** D **15.** B **Completion** **16.** chitin **17.** haploid **18.** club **19.** enzymes **20.** wheat **Short Answer** **21.** The hyphae on the left have cross walls dividing them into individual cells, while the hyphae on the right have no cross walls and thus contain many nuclei in a single chamber. **22.** Rhizoids anchor the fungus, secrete digestive enzymes, and absorb nutrients. **23.** An untrained person cannot tell the difference between poisonous and nonpoisonous mushrooms and should never eat wild fungi. **24.** Fungi are most important as decomposers.

Without decomposers, organic molecules would remain tied up in the bodies of dead organisms. **25.** Lichens gradually break down the rocks on which they grow. **Using Science Skills** **26.** opposite mating types (+ and –) **27.** Structure B, the zygospore, probably would become dormant until its environmental conditions improved. **28.** Zygomycota **29.** II **30.** The zygospore is 2N and is formed by the fusion of gametes of opposite mating types. **Essay** **31.** During the greater part of their life cycle, the nuclei of most fungi are haploid. Diploid nuclei form during sexual reproduction. Shortly after the nuclei fuse, however, meiosis occurs and produces haploid nuclei that dominate the remainder of the life cycle. **32.** The four phyla are Zygomycota (common molds), Ascomycota (sac fungi), Basidiomycota (club fungi), and Deuteromycota (imperfect fungi). Classification is based on their pattern of sexual reproduction. **33.** The fruiting body of a mushroom begins as a mass of growing hyphae that forms a button, or thick bulge, at the soil's surface. The button expands into a fruiting body that consists of a cap at the top of a stalk. The cap is composed of tightly packed hyphae, and the underside of the cap is composed of gills—thin blades of tissues lined with basidia that produce basidiospores. A mushroom can spring up overnight as the cells of the hyphae enlarge by rapidly taking in water. **34.** Some helpful fungi produce the antibiotic penicillin, make bread rise, are good to eat, and break down dead organisms. Harmful fungi cause ringworm, athlete's foot, and other human and animal diseases, and they cause many serious plant diseases that destroy food crops. **35.** Some bacteria are beneficial and keep other organisms such as fungi from growing out of control. Killing the body's normal bacteria can result in an overgrowth of yeasts, which cause thrush and reproductive tract infections.

Chapter 21—Test B
Multiple Choice **1.** B **2.** A **3.** C **4.** C **5.** C **6.** C **7.** C **8.** A **9.** C **10.** B **11.** C **12.** C **13.** B **14.** C **15.** C **Completion** **16.** Asexual **17.** caps **18.** sexual **19.** mycorrhizae **20.** lichen **Short Answer** **21.** Individual threads of fungi are hyphae; together they form a mycelium. **22.** Two nuclei are found in each cell; cells are separated by cross walls. **23.** baking and brewing **24.** The fruiting body of basidiomycetes is shaped like a club. **25.** Examples include any food crop disease caused by fungi, such as rusts or mildews. **Using Science Skills** **26.** One fruiting body is shown. **27.** Both are composed of hyphae. **28.** the mycelium **29.** No; a mycelium could be completely buried and thus be undetectable. **30.** It is a reproductive structure.

Unit 6—Test A

Multiple Choice 1. B 2. D 3. B 4. A 5. A 6. C
7. C 8. D 9. C 10. B 11. D 12. B 13. A 14. D
15. C **Completion** 16. cocci 17. retroviruses
18. antibiotics 19. phytoplankton 20. imperfect
Short Answer 21. Archaebacteria lack the peptidoglycan of eubacteria and also have different membrane lipids. The DNA sequences of key
archaebacterial genes are more like those of eukaryotes than those of eubacteria. 22. Antibiotics are
compounds that block the growth and reproduction
of bacteria. Viruses are not bacteria, and viruses have
few of the characteristics of living things. 23. Like
land plants, green algae have cellulose in their cell
walls, contain chlorophyll *a* and *b*, and store food in
the form of starch. 24. Alternation of generations is
the switching back and forth between haploid and
diploid stages during an organism's life cycle.
25. They recycle nutrients by breaking down the
bodies and wastes of other organisms. **Using
Science Skills** 26. Figure 2 shows the life cycle of a
bread mold. 27. The figure depicts the life cycle of a
common mold. Section I shows the process of asexual
reproduction, and section II shows the process of sexual reproduction. 28. The two structures are hyphae
called stolons, and they are of opposite mating types.
29. That structure is a zygospore. The opposite
mating types fused to form gametangia. Haploid
gametes in the gametangia then fused to form
zygotes, which developed into zygospores.
30. When conditions are favorable, the zygospore
germinates and undergoes meiosis, and then haploid
spores are released. This sexual process produces
new combinations of genetic information that may
help the organism meet changing environmental conditions. **Essay** 31. A typical eubacterium is a unicellular organism with a cell wall and a cell
membrane. It lacks a nucleus; its DNA is found within the cytoplasm. The cell moves with its flagella.
32. In a lytic infection, a bacteriophage injects DNA
into a bacterium and then takes over the bacterium's
metabolism, causing synthesis of new bacteriophage
proteins and nucleic acids, which assemble into viral
particles. The bacteriophage then lyses the bacterium's cell wall, releasing the bacteriophage particles.
33. Malaria is caused by the sporozoan *Plasmodium*.
The sporozoan is spread through bites of the female
Anopheles mosquito. 34. The bodies of multicellular
fungi are composed of thin filaments called hyphae.
Many hyphae are tangled together into a thick mass
called a mycelium, which can absorb food. A reproductive structure called a fruiting body grows above
ground from the mycelium in the soil beneath it.
35. Mycorrhizae are mutualistic relationships of
plant roots and fungi. The fungi help the plant roots
absorb water and minerals from the soil, which are
essential for the growth of many plants.

Unit 6—Test B

Multiple Choice 1. B 2. B 3. C 4. C 5. B 6. A
7. C 8. A 9. C 10. B 11. C 12. B 13. A 14. B
15. C **Completion** 16. archaebacteria 17. antibiotics 18. pseudopodia 19. plants 20. hyphae
Short Answer 21. Sterilization by heat, use of disinfectants, and correct food storage and processing
22. A typical virus is composed of a core of DNA or
RNA surrounded by a protein coat. 23. The basis for
that classification is the way in which different
groups obtain nutrition. 24. Many algae switch back
and forth between haploid and diploid stages during
their life cycles. 25. The four main groups are the
zygomycetes, or common molds; the ascomycetes, or
sac fungi; the basidomycetes, or club fungi; and the
deuteromycetes, or imperfect fungi. **Using Science
Skills** 26. unicellular 27. Structure A represents a
cell wall. 28. The DNA is found free within the cytoplasm and not within a nucleus. 29. The flagellum is
a structure used in movement. 30. The organism is a
prokaryote, or a bacterium. Its characteristics include
a cell wall, a cell membrane, DNA but no nucleus,
and flagella used in movement.

Flowchart

Topic:

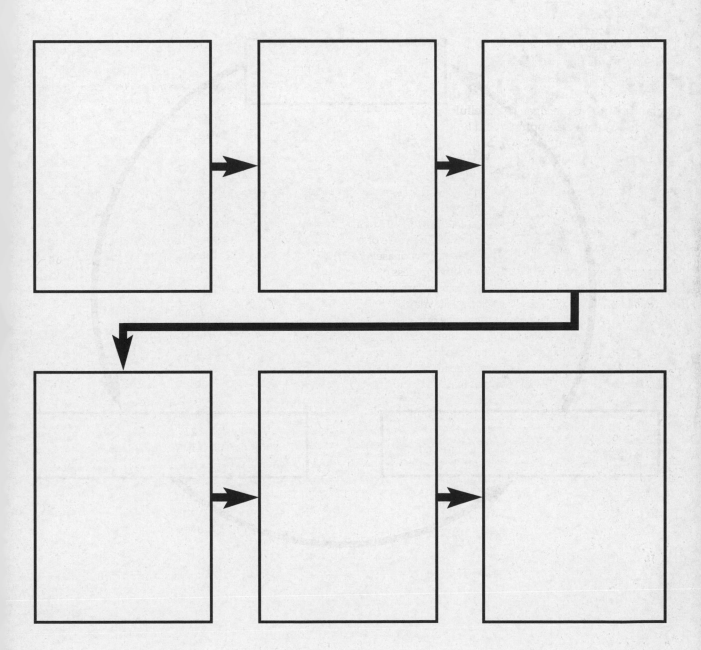

Cycle Diagram

Topic:

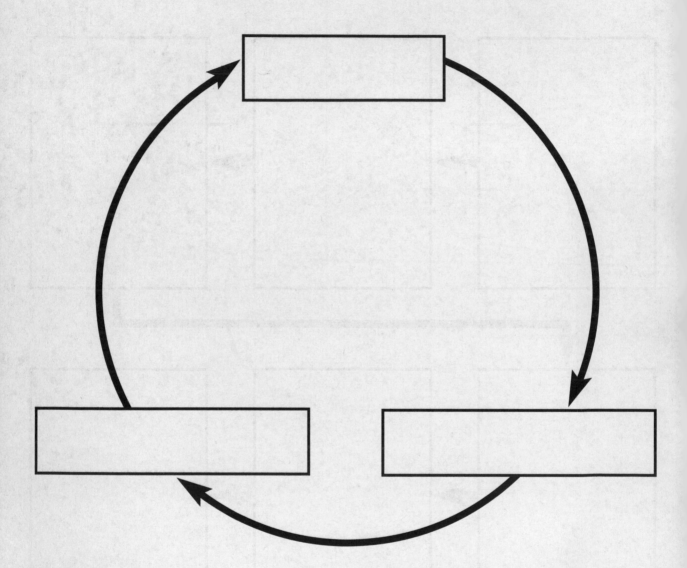

Name_____ Class_____ Date _____

Concept Circle

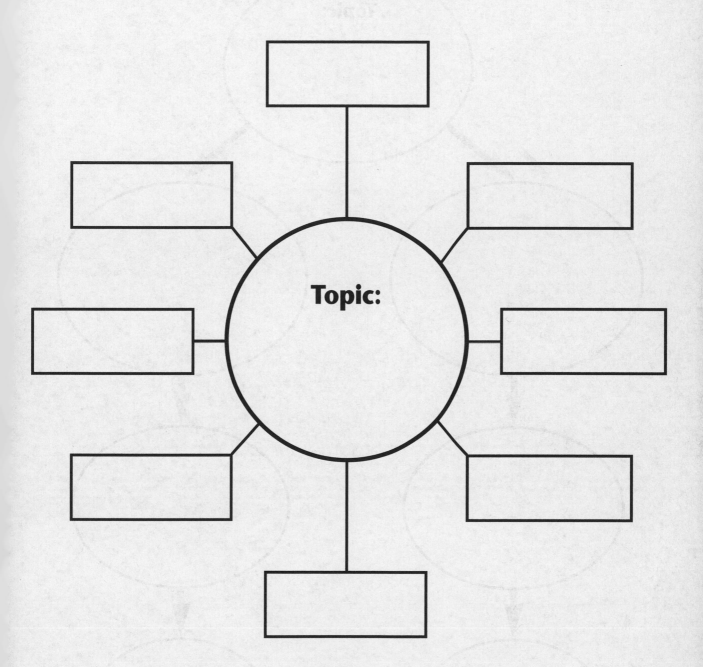

Modified Concept Map

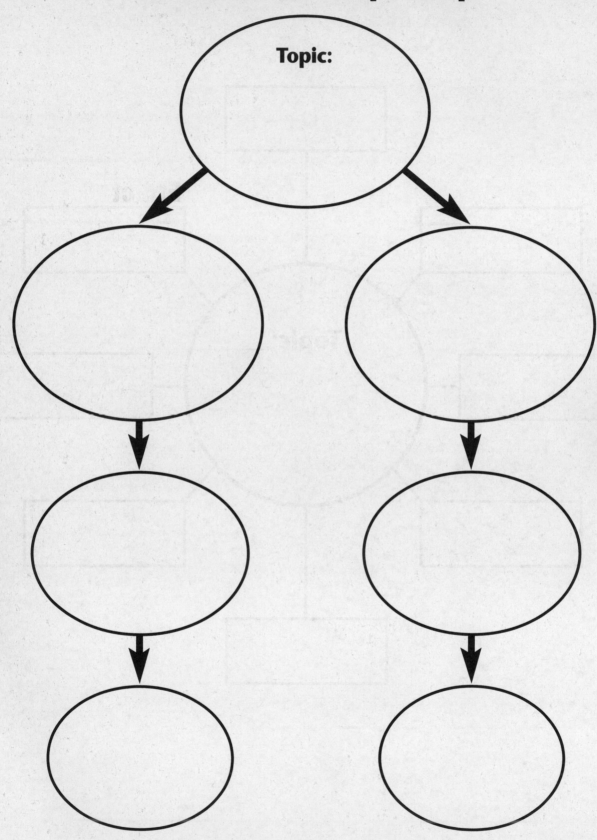

Topic:

Cause/Effect Chart

Topic:

Cause	Effect

Compare/Contrast Chart

Topic:

Similarities	Differences

Name_____ Class_____ Date _____

Venn Diagram

Topic: **Topic:**

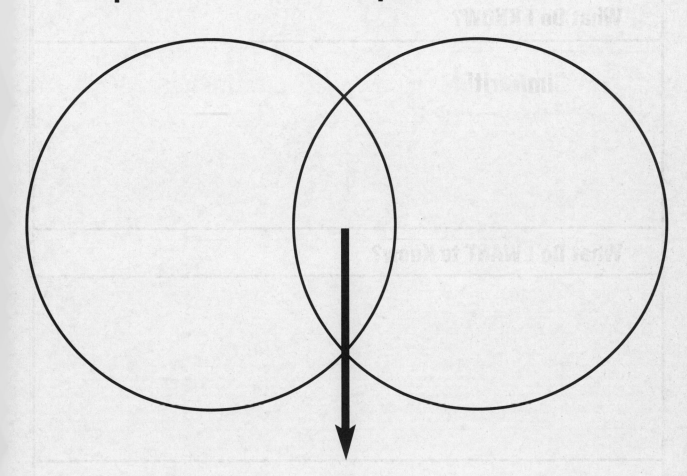

KWL Chart

Topic:

What Do I KNOW?
What Do I WANT to Know?
What Have I LEARNED?

Under the Microscope

Microorganisms are living things that can only be seen through a microscope. Imagine that you have just discovered a new microorganism. The first thing that you want to do is to tell the scientific community all about your new discovery.

1. Describe your microorganism in detail.

2. Describe its habitat.

3. Classify your microorganism by giving it a genus and species based on its characteristics.

19–1 Bacteria

A. Classifying Prokaryotes
   1. Eubacteria
   2. Archaebacteria
B. Identifying Prokaryotes
   1. Shapes
   2. Cell Walls
   3. Movement
C. Metabolic Diversity
   1. Heterotrophs
   2. Autotrophs
   3. Releasing Energy
D. Growth and Reproduction
   1. Binary Fission
   2. Conjugation
   3. Spore Formation
E. Importance of Bacteria
   1. Decomposers
   2. Nitrogen Fixers
   3. Human Uses of Bacteria

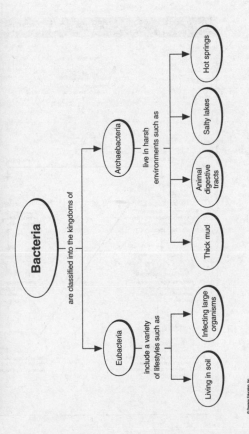

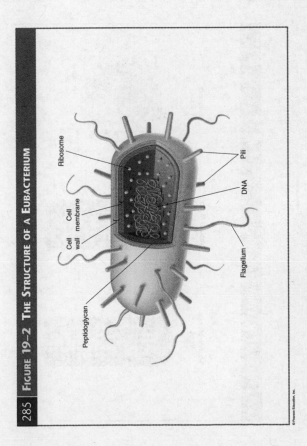

What Viruses Mean to You

If you have ever had a cold, you are probably familiar with the word *virus*. It is a word that makes most people frown.

1. What do you think of when you hear the word *virus*? Make a list of all the words you can think of that relate to viruses.

2. What are two things that you would like to find out about viruses?

19–2 Viruses

A. What Is a Virus?

B. Viral Infection

   1. Lytic Infection

   2. Lysogenic Infection

C. Retroviruses

D. Viruses and Living Cells

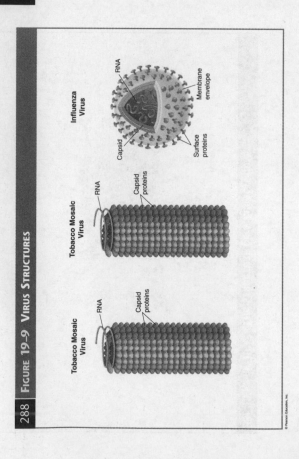

FIGURE 19–9 VIRUS STRUCTURES

288

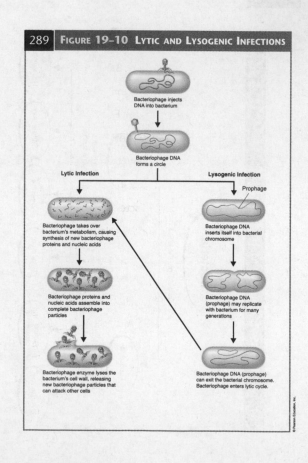

289 | FIGURE 19–10 LYTIC AND LYSOGENIC INFECTIONS

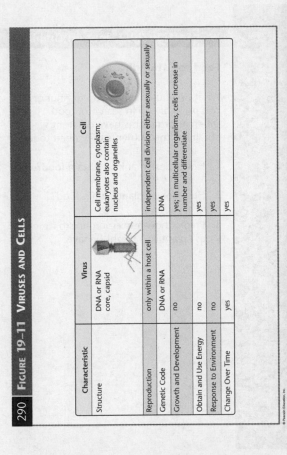

Characteristic	Virus	Cell
Structure	DNA or RNA core, capsid	Cell membrane, cytoplasm; eukaryotes also contain nucleus and organelles
Reproduction	only within a host cell	independent cell division either asexually or sexually
Genetic Code	DNA or RNA	DNA
Growth and Development	no	yes; in multicellular organisms, cells increase in number and differentiate
Obtain and Use Energy	no	yes
Response to Environment	no	yes
Change Over Time	yes	yes

© Pearson Education, Inc.

Bacteria vs. Humans

Bacteria are all around you—in the air you breathe, under your feet, on your skin, and even in your body! They may be tiny, but they can still have an impact on your life.

Use what you already know about bacteria to answer these questions.

1. In what ways are bacteria similar to humans?

2. In what ways are bacteria different from humans?

3. How can bacteria be harmful?

ANSWERS
1. Like humans, bacteria are alive and some can move. Both obtain energy, exchange gases, grow, and reproduce.
2. Unlike humans, bacteria are extremely small, some can live in harsher environments and without oxygen, some bacteria use sunlight to produce their own food.
3. Bacteria cause diseases, release poisonous chemicals, and compete with humans for food.

© Pearson Education, Inc.

19-3 Diseases Caused by Bacteria and Viruses

A. Bacterial Disease in Humans

   1. Using Cells for Food

   2. Releasing Toxins

   3. Preventing Bacterial Disease

B. Bacterial Disease in Animals

C. Controlling Bacteria

   1. Sterilization by Heat

   2. Disinfectants

   3. Food Storage and Processing

D. Viral Disease in Humans

E. Viral Disease in Animals

F. Viral Disease in Plants

G. Viroids and Prions

   1. Viroids

   2. Prions

© Pearson Education, Inc.

Disease	Pathogen	Prevention
Tooth decay	Streptococcus mutans	Regular dental hygiene
Lyme disease	Borrelia burgdorferi	Protection from tick bites
Tetanus	Clostridium tetani	Current tetanus vaccination
Tuberculosis	Mycobacterium tuberculosis	Vaccination
Salmonella food poisoning	Salmonella enteritidis	Proper food-handling practices
Pneumonia	Streptococcus pneumoniae	Maintaining good health
Cholera	Vibrio cholerae	Clean water supplies

© Pearson Education, Inc.

Type of Virus	Nucleic Acid	Disease
Oncogenic viruses	DNA	Cancer
Retroviruses	RNA	Cancer, AIDS
Adenoviruses	DNA	Respiratory infections
Herpesviruses	DNA	Chickenpox
Poxviruses	DNA	Smallpox

© Pearson Education, Inc.

Food for Thought

What do you do when you get hungry? You probably go in search of food. Different organisms have different ways of obtaining the nutrients they need to live.

1. How does an animal obtain food?

2. How does a plant obtain food?

3. Predict how a microorganism described as "plantlike" might behave.

ANSWERS
1. An animal obtains food by eating plants or other animals.
2. A plant obtains food by the process of photosynthesis.
3. If the microorganism is plantlike, then it may obtain its food by the process of photosynthesis.

© Pearson Education, Inc.

20–1 The Kingdom Protista

A. What Is a Protist?

B. Evolution of Protists

C. Classification of Protists

© Pearson Education, Inc.

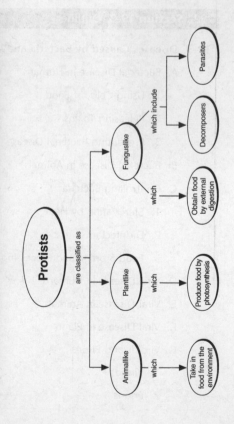

© Pearson Education, Inc.

On the Move

Think about the last time you watched a puppy at play, a fish in an aquarium, or a squirrel in the park. They don't stay still for long. How do they get where they are going?

1. List five different ways in which animals can move from place to place.

2. What structures do these animals have that enable them to move?

3. What structures might a microorganism need in order to move?

ANSWERS
1. Possible answers: walking or crawling, flying, swimming, burrowing
2. Legs, feet, arms, wings, fins, to name a few.
3. Students may suggest that microorganisms need structures similar to that of arms, legs, or fins.

20–2 Animallike Protists: Protozoans

A. Zooflagellates

B. Sarcodines

C. Ciliates

    1. Internal Anatomy

    2. Conjugation

D. Sporozoans

E. Animallike Protists and Disease

    1. Malaria

    2. Other Protistan Diseases

F. Ecology of Animallike Protists

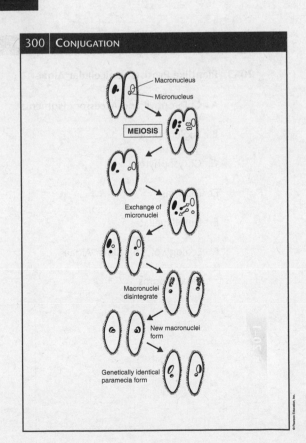

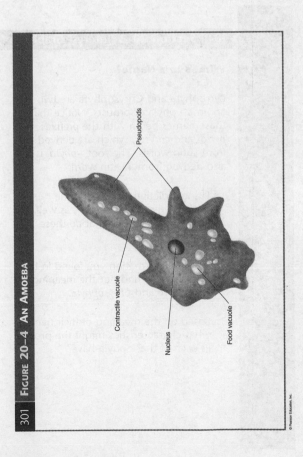

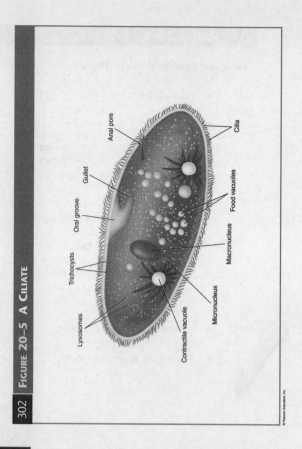

Anal pore
Gullet
Oral groove
Trichocysts
Lysosomes
Contractile vacuole
Micronucleus
Macronucleus
Food vacuoles
Cilia

© Pearson Education, Inc.

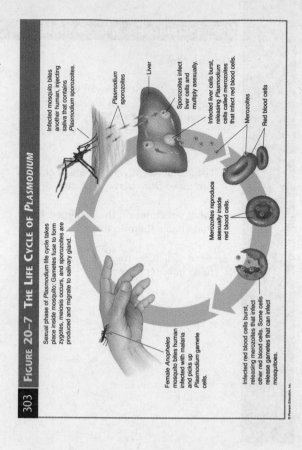

Sexual phase of *Plasmodium* life cycle takes place inside mosquito. Gametes fuse to form zygotes, meiosis occurs, and sporozoites are produced and migrate to salivary gland.

Infected mosquito bites another human, injecting saliva that contains *Plasmodium* sporozoites.

Plasmodium sporozoites

Liver

Sporozoites infect liver cells and multiply asexually.

Infected liver cells burst, releasing *Plasmodium* cells called merozoites that infect red blood cells.

Merozoites

Red blood cells

Merozoites reproduce asexually inside red blood cells.

Female *Anopheles* mosquito bites human infected with malaria and picks up *Plasmodium* gamete cells.

Infected red blood cells burst, releasing merozoites that infect other red blood cells. Some cells release gametes that can infect mosquitoes.

© Pearson Education, Inc.

What's in a Name?

Pyrrophyta and Chrysophyta are two common phyla of protists. Notice that these names begin with the prefixes *pyrro-* and *chryso-*, which are derived from Latin words. The root, *-phyta,* is also derived from a Latin word.

1. Using a dictionary, look up the prefixes *pyrro-* and *chryso-*, as well as the root *-phyta*. What do these terms mean?

2. Use the information you found in the dictionary to find out the meaning of *Pyrrophyta* and *Chrysophyta.*

3. Based on the meaning of their names, what characteristics might the protists in each of these phyla have?

20-3 Plantlike Protists: Unicellular Algae

A. Chlorophyll and Accessory Pigments

B. Euglenophytes

C. Chrysophytes

D. Diatoms

E. Dinoflagellates

F. Ecology of Unicellular Algae

Algal Blooms

© Pearson Education, Inc.

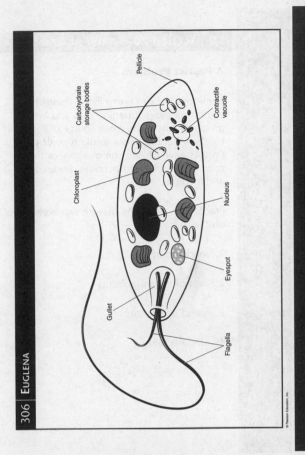

Pellicle

Carbohydrate storage bodies

Contractile vacuole

Chloroplast

Nucleus

Eyespot

Gullet

Flagella

Sargasso Sea Story

Many square kilometers of the open Atlantic Ocean between the islands of the Azores and the Bahamas are covered by huge, floating protists called *Sargassum*. Known as the Sargasso Sea, this area of warm water is named for the brown protists that dominate its surface.

1. Why do you think *Sargassum* and other similar protists are called seaweeds?

2. Compare and contrast *Sargassum* to another type of brown algae you have read about in this chapter. How are they different?

ANSWERS
1. Students may say that these protists look like large weeds that grow in the sea.
2. Students will likely know that some algae are multicellular, but most of the algae they have read about so far are unicellular.

20–4 Plantlike Protists: Red, Brown, and Green Algae

A. Red Algae

B. Brown Algae

C. Green Algae

   1. Unicellular Green Algae

   2. Colonial Green Algae

   3. Multicellular Green Algae

D. Reproduction in Green Algae

   1. Reproduction in *Chlamydomonas*

   2. Reproduction in *Ulva*

E. Human Uses of Algae

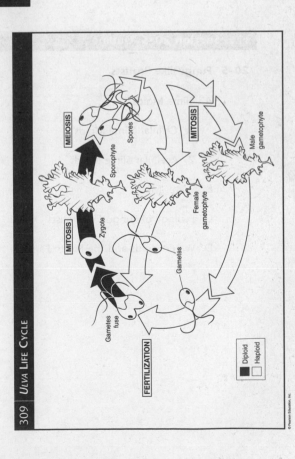

MEIOSIS

Spores

MITOSIS

Sporophyte

Male gametophyte

MITOSIS

Zygote

Female gametophyte

Gametes

Gametes fuse

FERTILIZATION

Diploid
Haploid

FIGURE 20–17 THE LIFE CYCLE OF CHLAMYDOMONAS

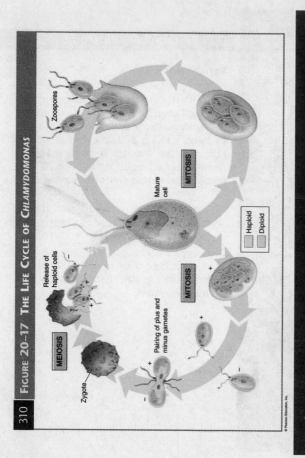

Zoospores

MITOSIS

Mature cell

Haploid
Diploid

MITOSIS

Release of haploid cells

+
+
+
+

MEIOSIS

Pairing of plus and minus gametes

+

Zygote

+

+

–
–
–

© Pearson Education, Inc.

A Protist Problem

Some protists can harm living things by causing diseases. Imagine that you live on an island where the main source of food for the inhabitants is a single type of plant. Protists have caused the majority of the crop of that plant to become diseased and inedible.

Predict the effect the disease will likely have on the following:

1. food supply

2. lives of the inhabitants

3. island ecosystem

4. island economy

© Pearson Education, Inc.

20–5 Funguslike Protists

A. Slime Molds

   1. Cellular Slime Molds

   2. Acellular Slime Molds

B. Water Molds

C. Ecology of Funguslike Protists

D. Water Molds and the Potato Famine

© Pearson Education, Inc.

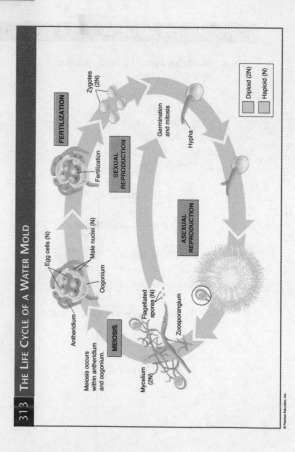

Zygotes (2N)

FERTILIZATION

Germination and mitosis

Diploid (2N)
Haploid (N)

Fertilization

SEXUAL REPRODUCTION

Hypha

Egg cells (N)

Male nuclei (N)

ASEXUAL REPRODUCTION

Oogonium

Antheridium

Flagellated spores (N)

Meiosis occurs within antheridium and oogonium.

MEIOSIS

Zoosporangium

Mycelium (2N)

© Pearson Education, Inc.

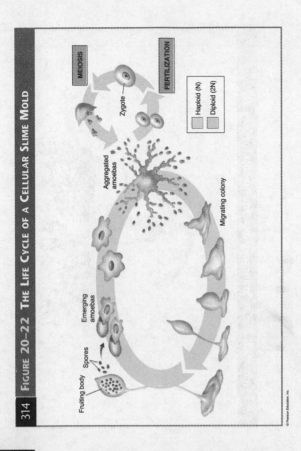

FIGURE 20–22 THE LIFE CYCLE OF A CELLULAR SLIME MOLD

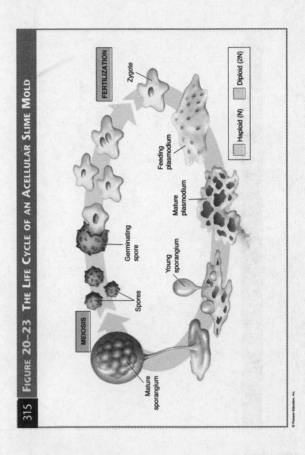

FIGURE 20–23 THE LIFE CYCLE OF AN ACELLULAR SLIME MOLD

Animal, Vegetable, or Mineral?

Have you ever eaten mushrooms? Perhaps you have seen them growing from the ground in a forest or yard. Perhaps you have seen them for sale in a supermarket.

1. What are some things that you know about mushrooms?

2. Would you classify mushrooms as an animal, a plant, or something else? Give reasons for your answer.

21–1 The Kingdom Fungi

A. What Are Fungi?

B. Structure and Function of Fungi

C. Reproduction in Fungi

D. How Fungi Spread

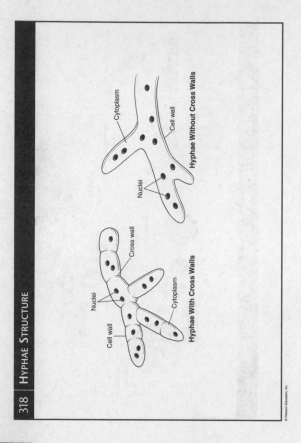

© Pearson Education, Inc.

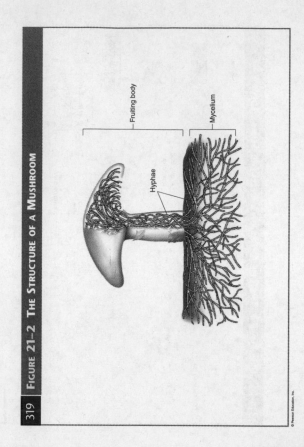

© Pearson Education, Inc.

Fungi and You

Believe it or not, fungi play an important role in your life. The bread you eat, the salad you make, and the medicine that you take when you are sick may include various types of fungi.

1. List as many examples of fungi that you can.

2. How are fungi helpful to humans?

3. How are fungi harmful to humans?

ANSWERS
1. Mushrooms, mold, yeast, mildew, truffles
2. They are sources of food and are used in making bread, wine, and medicines.
3. Some are poisonous and can cause illness or death.

© Pearson Education, Inc.

21–2 Classification of Fungi

A. The Common Molds

1. Structure and Function of Bread Mold

2. Life Cycle of Molds

B. The Sac Fungi

1. Life Cycle of Sac Fungi

2. Yeasts

C. The Club Fungi

1. Life Cycle of Club Fungi

2. Diversity of Club Fungi

3. Edible and Inedible Mushrooms

D. The Imperfect Fungi

© Pearson Education, Inc.

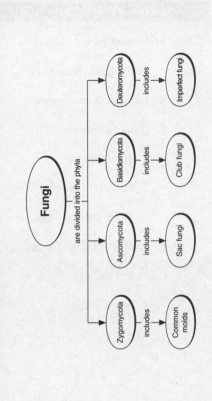

© Pearson Education, Inc.

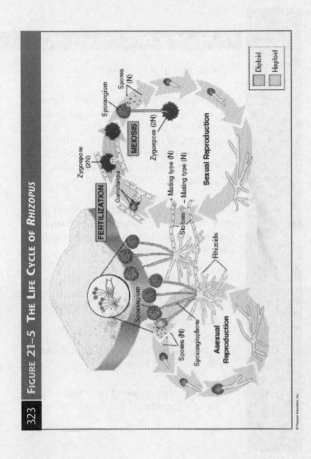

© Pearson Education, Inc.

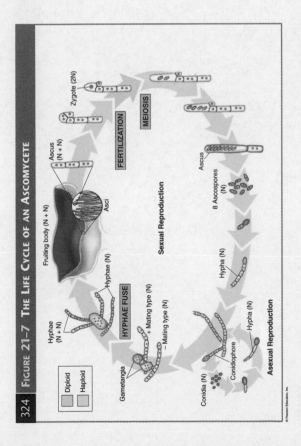

© Pearson Education, Inc.

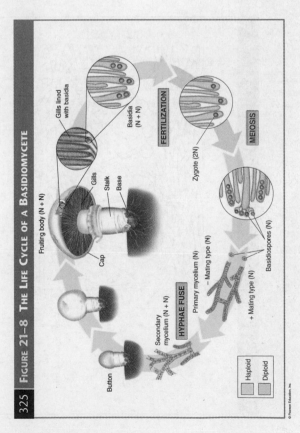

© Pearson Education, Inc.

Which Fungi Are They?

You may recall that decomposers break down the remains of other organisms. Parasites are organisms that harm other organisms while living on or within them. Some live in close contact and form a mutually beneficial association with other species.

Classify each of the following fungi as decomposers, parasites, or organisms that live in a mutually beneficial relationship with another species.

1. A network of fungi covers the roots of fir trees. The trees provide the fungi with food, and the fungi help the tree roots absorb water.

2. Fungi living on growing corn stalks destroy corn kernels.

3. Mushrooms growing on a fallen log obtain food from the decaying wood.

© Pearson Education, Inc.

21–3 Ecology of Fungi

A. All Fungi Are Heterotrophs

B. Fungi as Decomposers

C. Fungi as Parasites

   1. Plant Diseases

   2. Human Diseases

   3. Other Animal Diseases

D. Symbiotic Relationships

   1. Lichens

   2. Mycorrhizae

© Pearson Education, Inc.

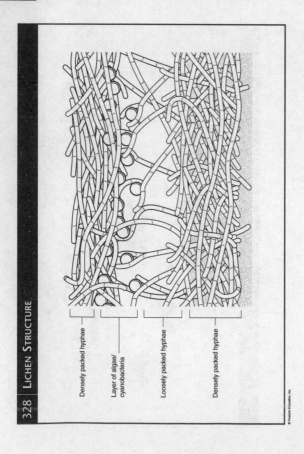

Densely packed hyphae

Layer of algae/cyanobacteria

Loosely packed hyphae

Densely packed hyphae

© Pearson Education, Inc.